LESSONS IN LEARNING AND LEADERSHIP:
A Staff College for NHS Wales

Stephen Prosser & Siobhan McClelland

TRAFFORD

Note for Librarians: A cataloguing record for this book is available from Library and Archives Canada at www.collectionscanada.ca/amicus/index-e.html
ISBN 1-4120-2925-2

Printed in Victoria, BC, Canada. Printed on paper with minimum 30% recycled fibre. Trafford's print shop runs on "green energy" from solar, wind and other environmentally-friendly power sources.

TRAFFORD.
PUBLISHING™
Offices in Canada, USA, Ireland and UK

Book sales for North America and international:
Trafford Publishing, 6E–2333 Government St.,
Victoria, BC V8T 4P4 CANADA
phone 250 383 6864 (toll-free 1 888 232 4444)
fax 250 383 6804; email to orders@trafford.com
Book sales in Europe:
Trafford Publishing (UK) Limited, 9 Park End Street, 2nd Floor
Oxford, UK OX1 1HH UNITED KINGDOM
phone +44 (0)1865 722 113 (local rate 0845 230 9601)
facsimile +44 (0)1865 722 868; info.uk@trafford.com
Order online at:
trafford.com/04-0753

10 9 8 7 6 5 4 3

Acknowledgments

We would like to acknowledge the help of all those who have supported us in the production of this book. We would particularly like to thank Andrew Price for his comments on the manuscript, Stephen Redmond for his commitment through the funding of the Staff College, and Paul Williams for his chairmanship of the College throughout its existence.

Dedication

"A three stranded cord is not easily broken"

Glossary

CPD	Continuing Professional Development
GP	General Practitioner
IHSM	Institute of Healthcare Management
ICT	Information, Communications and Technology
IMT	Information, Management and Technology
LHG	Local Health Group
MAS	Management Advisory Service
MCS	Manpower Consultancy Services
NHS	National Health Service
OD	Organisation Development
PAM	Profession Allied to Medicine
PDP	Personal Development Plan
SID	Strategic Intent and Direction (for Wales)
SPR	Specialist Registrar
UWCM	University of Wales College of Medicine
WHCSA	Welsh Health Common Services Authority
WHPF	Welsh Health Planning Forum

Contents

Acknowledgments iii

Dedication v

Glossary vi

1   Introduction 1

2   The Genesis 5

3   Moving from Idea to Reality 15

4   The 'Ipso Facto' Staff College 27

5   Goodbye Old College...Hello New College 37

6   Funding the New College 43

7   Staff College Activities 47

8   Staff College Programmes 57

9   An Evidence Base for the Staff College 63

10   Reviewing the College 69

11   Conclusions 75

Postscript 81

Appendix 1   Heronston Meeting Invitees 83

Appendix 2   Management Group 85

Appendix 3   NHS Staff College Fellows 87

1

Introduction

The NHS Staff College Wales was formally established in January 1995. It had taken over ten years to get to the point at which the National Health Service (NHS) in Wales could be served by a staff college with a mission to develop management and leadership amongst general managers and clinicians alike and help change managerial and organisational cultures. The introduction of general management to the NHS, following the 'Griffiths Report' of 1984, created a cadre of general managers who held responsibility for the running of health services. Prior to this the language of administration and consensus management dominated the running of the NHS. Over the next decade emphasis was also increasingly placed on involving clinicians in management to recognise the key role that doctors in particular played in the allocation of healthcare resources. Whilst developing managerial skills and knowledge was considered important within the NHS, leadership, which could more readily be seen to span both the clinical and managerialist perspectives, became even more important.

The Griffiths Report on General Management was followed some five years later by the "Working for Patients" White Paper produced by the then Thatcher administration. It was this document that ushered in the era of the 'internal market' with a greater emphasis on competition and the business and market based skills that would support the development of a quasi market in healthcare. The introduction of business style principles into the NHS included cash limited budgets, value for money, compulsory competitive tendering and cost improvement programmes. These were just some of the initiatives enacted in the name of the dominant driver of efficiency. Whilst there has been much debate as to how far market principles really permeated the NHS the split between the purchasers or commissioners of healthcare and those who provided health care services was to continue to dominate the structure of the NHS in England and Wales into the New Labour era of 1997 onwards.

The election of New Labour did, however, witness a further shift towards collaboration and partnership working, for example between health and social care agencies in Wales and with the private sector in England. In England concepts of modernisation, highly target driven and focusing on the continuous improvement of healthcare services, were to dominate the NHS agenda. At the end of its first, and particularly during the second, administration of New Labour the NHS saw significant increases in funding but ones which were increasingly tied to achievement of modernisation targets. Derek Wanless' review of NHS funding, conducted for the Treasury, concluded that general taxation remained the preferred option for the future funding of the NHS in the UK. In England this was combined with a new structural initiative in the introduction of Foundation Trusts and the emergence of the 'Choice' agenda as a new mechanism for incentivising the NHS.

1999 also saw devolution for Scotland, Northern Ireland and Wales. Health and health services became a devolved matter and in Wales occupied the largest proportion of the Welsh Assembly's budget and the considerable attention of Welsh politicians. The devolution settlements offered a challenge to the concept of a <u>National</u> Health Service with different structures and priorities emerging. Thus in Scotland the vestiges of the internal market were abandoned and in Wales the 2001 'Improving Health in Wales: A National Plan for the NHS and its Partners' saw an emphasis on partnership working between health and local government. This was coupled with an emphasis on public health and the reduction of health inequalities through community engagement and empowerment. Derek Wanless was also seen in Wales where he acted as an advisor to the review of health and social care in the principality.

The emergence and development of the Staff College occurred during a lengthy yet dynamic period of change for the NHS in which managers and leaders emerged and in which the structure and organisation of the NHS changed and continued to change radically. The Staff College was innovative within the NHS. Whilst similar colleges had developed within other organisations, both in the public and private sectors, the NHS had not provided such a facility to its staff. The tale of the quest to establish this college in Wales is therefore an important one to tell. It offers insight not just into the developmental needs of the National Health Service, both in terms of its staff and its organisation, but also into the policy environment in which new organisations can both flourish and fail.

This book seeks to tell the story of the NHS Staff College Wales. It traces the development of the college from early ideas through to its establishment and delivery of programmes, development interventions and research. The story concludes in 2001 at the point at which the NHS Staff College Wales is transformed into the Centre for Health Leadership Wales. The book is based on an extensive analysis of archived NHS Staff College documentation combined with views from those working within the College from its early to its current days.

2

The Genesis

The genesis of the idea of a Staff College for the NHS in Wales emerged in the late 1980s. Until the advent of devolution, culminating in the first elections to the National Assembly for Wales in 1999, the NHS in Wales had been perceived as an adjunct to the English NHS. Whilst there is some merit in this argument there were notable exceptions to this rubberstamping of Department of Health policies. The All Wales Strategies for Mental Handicap and Mental Health were pioneering within a UK context. The creation of the Welsh Health Planning Forum which championed the concept of 'health gain' was also a distinctive development. It is perhaps not coincidental that the notion of a Staff College emerged at the same time as the creation of the Welsh Health Planning Forum (WHPF). Both Staff College and WHPF formed part of the strategic view of the then Director of NHS Wales John Wyn Owen.

Perhaps the first mention of a Staff College for Wales comes in notes from the All Wales Personnel Committee of 1984. This states that the Committee considered the issue and favoured a *"college without walls"* approach. This issue of the physical entity of the Staff College was to play an important part in discussions regarding both the creation and development of the organisation.

The Deloitte, Haskins and Sells report of 1987 "Report on the Provision of a Training Centre: Welsh Health Authorities", which examined the feasibility of the NHS in Wales owning its own training centre, highlights another important tension: the emphasis on training at this point and the differences between concepts of training and development and between individual, group and organisational interventions. Training for administrators and subsequently managers had had some central direction but had traditionally been the preserve of local NHS organisations such as management units and later NHS Trusts. The respective roles of locality and centre in providing training and development opportunities was one which was also to be of significance in setting up and then developing the college.

The Deloitte report cites the impact of general management, arising from the Griffiths report of 1984, which led to the demise of consensus management and the introduction of general management into the NHS, as being significant in requiring *"a fundamental change in the organisation"*. Moreover, the report states *"This also requires a new corporate image"*. As will be seen, issues of managerialism and corporateness also play a strong part in the initial discussions regarding the Staff College's formation. The report also locates itself within the still raging debate regarding managerialism and professionalism and a need for common training:

"There appears to be an overall lack of a corporate identity within the NHS with few staff taking pride in the achievement of their organisation. They tend to think of themselves as either belonging to a specific authority or profession and thus not working to corporate objectives

Obviously one of the key methods to help facilitate the break from the past is through providing common management development and training programmes."

The report also identified the tension between centralisation and decentralisation and the need for the College to be clearly located within the NHS family:

"...although these (schemes) should be administered from the Centre in order to promote consistency of approach and standard, it is important for the individual authorities to keep their autonomy, so that they do not perceive the centre as dictating to them"

The notion of central diktat versus local ownership is a common thread in public service management and delivery and one which continues to impact throughout the United Kingdom.

The Deloitte report concludes that a *"neutral training ground which is common to all authorities, and which can promote an all-Wales corporate image, both internally and externally"* could address some of these tensions and that an all-Wales training centre was the means by which this could be achieved. The report states that whilst Swansea University was predominantly used to train staff, and to a high standard, that this did not promote *"corporate identity"* and that the proposed training centre would give *"NHS staff something to identify with and be proud of"*. Moreover the centre would allow staff to *"widen their knowledge and as a result of this be better in-formed about the NHS"*.

Whilst the Deloitte report offers the services of Deloitte in pur-suing the option appraisal for the development of a training centre there appears to be something of a hiatus until the somewhat moved on concept of a Staff College re-emerges in 1989 which saw the de-velopment of a concept paper on the subject. The use of language is important with the move from training centre to staff college and ultimately to leadership centre reflecting the values and fashions in management and policy both of the time and of the various stake-holders. The late 1980s were thus dominated by the introduction of general management and the need to develop business style manage-rial skills and knowledge amongst managers and clinicians.

The re-emergence of a "Health Services Staff College" has per-haps an opportunistic link to it given the availability at this point of a potential physical location on the Swansea University campus. This reflects the burgeoning discipline of management science which was gaining greater credibility in academic circles and the positioning of Swansea University in providing training for the NHS. As important-ly it reflects the place of a key player who was both an academic and a Chair of a Health Authority.

The link between a staff college for the NHS and academia is another thread which runs through the history of NHS Staff College Wales. This reflects an important debate, between the need and place for training and development for the NHS, and the place for an en-vironment and organisation in which ideas and cutting edge thinking in respect of management, organisation development and ultimately leadership within the NHS could be progressed.

In developing the Staff College the place of stakeholders was in-strumental in facilitating and hampering progress. In the document of 1989 initially discussing the Staff College it is stated that there is *"a strong enthusiasm in the Welsh Office Directorate for the initia-tive"*. In 1989 responsibility for NHS Wales lay within the remit of the Secretary of State for Wales and the civil servants within the Welsh Office. The NHS Directorate, headed up by the Director of the NHS in Wales, was located within the Welsh Office. Beneath this were the Health Authorities including the Welsh Health Common Services Authority (WHCSA) that provided a range of services to the Health Authorities of Wales. These included IT and Estates, supplies, certain clinical services, human resources, organisation development and training services. It should be noted that this initial phase predates the introduction of the internal market leaving Health Authorities as the pre-eminent organisations within NHS Wales.

The debate regarding the objectives of any Staff College was also to dominate its history. This is in part a reflection of the practice/ideas tension and the views and requirements of the stakeholders. By March of 1989 at a meeting of Chairmen of the Health Authorities, following the discussion of the concept paper, the notes of the meeting state:

"The proposal that an NHS Staff College which would contribute to promoting the corporateness of the NHS in Wales should be established was one which was raised before. However there was now for example one opportunity to provide such a college through leasing facilities at a new development at the University College Swansea and without incurring any capital costs...

- *The proposal of a staff college was supported in principle by the Chairmen's group*
- *In establishing a college (s) the needs of all areas in Wales should be taken into account*
- *Detailed proposals and requirements for developing the staff college should be researched and presented for consideration"*

What should particularly be drawn from this is the view that the Staff College could promote the concept of corporateness within NHS Wales. Moreover, the discussion reflected familiar tension particularly between North and South Wales regarding the location of a college and its services. A view that the North of Wales suffers in respect of service provision and access to centralised Welsh resources has, in the eyes of some, only been exacerbated by devolution and the location of the National Assembly for Wales in Cardiff.

The paper produced by the Welsh Office's Manpower Steering Group supporting this discussion further reflects these issues:

"In recent times support for an NHS Staff College for Wales has been growing along with the recognition that people form the most important resource, and that their development is paramount. A staff college is seen as representing the corporateness of the NHS in Wales".

This further reflected the training and development versus 'think tank' debate:

*"The NHS in Wales runs a number of management and other cours-
es at the All Wales level... The Corporate Management Programme en-
visaged a stronger collaboration with the University sector in Wales".*

In relation to emergent managerialism the paper states:

*"Instead of being an almost random and certainly divergent, col-
lection of professions, objectives and facilities, the NHS in Wales is
becoming a managed service".*

This reflects a continuing discussion, within the emergence of
managerialism in public services, of the role of professions. In the
NHS this particularly focused on the medical profession which had
traditionally acted as the most powerful stakeholder. The attempt to
draw physicians into management and into the staff college fold was
also to become of importance.

The place for opportunism in developing any new idea, policy or
organisation was also clear. The availability of accommodation on the
Swansea University site provided the impetus to pushing forward the
idea. However, the idea of the Staff College having a distinct physical
entity, as seen in original discussions in 1984, was to continue to rage
particularly during the more market oriented 1990s.

Following the provisional acceptance of the idea of the college
by the Chairmen of the Health Authorities a paper was produced,
for internal consumption, within Manpower Consultancy Services
in WHCSA arguing the case for a staff college in advance of a final
paper being produced for wider circulation. This was the first docu-
mented point at which a definition of a Staff College was attempted:

*"...a staff college is an institution or collection of institutions where
the training and education of individuals, usually Managers or Of-
ficers, from a certain organisation is carried out. What distinguishes it
from a local authority college or management school is that it is owned
and run by an organisation for staff of that organisation. It contains
tutorial facilities and accommodation and may provide residential accommodation also".*

The issue of the employing organisation, in this case the NHS,
providing an educative, training and development institution links
closely with the notion of promoting corporate values. However, it

raises the issue of whether this can also be something which allows for critical and cutting edge thinking. The paper goes on to state:

"...Following the military and the private and public sector models, the staff college is a purveyor of the values and standards which an organisation promotes and upholds. Also it acts as a focus for, and a symbol of commitment to, excellence in the training and development of staff. This aspect of the staff college as a flagship, symbol and shaper and promoter of organisational ethos is at least as important a feature of staff colleges as the provision of educational accommodation".

This concept of the Staff College as one which promotes organisational ethos is worthy of further exploration. In terms of corporateness, and the debate regarding the role of a staff college in promoting this, the paper states:

"relationships with local colleges are of varying degrees of quality and the lack of shared objectives and background limits the extent to which even the best colleges can interpret the wishes of, and serve the NHS".

The paper also enters the debate regarding the need for a physical location for a Staff College:

"... these intangible, but significant, functions of a staff college mean that a single identifiable location is preferable to several. Certainly, the concept of a "staff college without walls" where universities, individuals, colleges and other facilities and locations become potentially, part of the flexibly defined staff college ignores the important symbolic and cultural role of the staff college".

The paper also reveals in the wake of the introduction of general management the growing importance of management training and development within the NHS:

"Now as never before the NHS in Wales has a strong management culture, enveloping all managers regardless of discipline which holds and applies the values that will make it a well managed and highly competitive organisation".

It is also interesting to note here the use of market oriented language reflecting that of the "Working for Patients" White Paper which also emerged in 1989 and which launched the introduction of the internal market within the NHS. The concept paper cites the

White Paper and is a further demonstration of the role of opportunism and the colonizing of new language to promote a development whose genesis predates the introduction of the market into health care services.

Whilst the paper states its purpose as arguing the case for a staff college it makes some limited suggestions as to the arguments against its establishment:

"The main arguments against staff colleges, and the reasons frequently given when staff colleges are closed down, revolve around cost and level of usage".

In September 1989 a revised and refined version of the paper appeared produced by the Manpower Consultancy Service of WHCSA at the request of the Welsh Office. Interestingly this paper plays down the role of Staff College as promoting organisational ethos and corporateness so prominent in the first paper. Moreover, the shift is away from emphasising the disparate nature of current provision, particularly within the NHS, and in fact embracing what is already offered and stating the role of a Staff College in supporting rather than replacing this. This may reflect the different authorship of the paper and the views of key stakeholders. It also seeks to recognise the protectiveness local organisations feel over local initiatives and a repeated concern regarding central control. As such it contributes to the debate which was to dominate the Staff College's existence: the need to remain part of and linked into the NHS which is of itself comprised of somewhat disparate organisations, professions and stakeholders.

"The promotion of a staff college does not in any way devalue or criticise the quality of training and facilities currently provided within health authorities and units. A staff college exists to support the training activities of others. The creation of a building, in whatever location, does not predetermine that all college training activities must be carried out within its walls. If this were the case the college might be seen as a fringe activity by local staff. The staff and associates of a staff college would be drawn from and employed by the NHS in Wales. The college cannot become an elite remote feature of NHS staff development."

Defining the Staff College has a somewhat different focus in this second paper:

"The term staff college is likely to conjure up various images rang-ing from the large industrial company model, typified by a large rural mansion, with sophisticated leisure facilities and luxurious ac-commodation to the 1960s/1970s university model with plain halls of residence, windswept grounds and basic lecture theatres. These images largely concentrate solely on the physical manifestations of a staff college. When faced with identifying the activities of staff colleges the opinions range from a central point for all training within an organi-sation to a collection of academics involved in policy analysis and oc-casional training for an exclusive few".

The paper goes on to identify the key activities of the staff col-lege:

"A staff college is an institution and collection of staff/associates whose task is to provide a corporate focus for the following activi-ties:
- *High quality training across all grades and profession which complements local training, with particular emphasis on management development*
- *Access to quality training facilities by the NHS (and other like minded organisations)*
- *Promotion of standards of excellence within staff development*
- *Analysis of new training methods and programmes*
- *Strategic analysis of organisational objectives and the resultant training needs*
- *Consultancy advice to authorities as required based on experience of the above activities"*

Overall the paper states that the Staff College can provide a "one stop" service in terms of activities and facilities. It is also stated that, subject to the usual caveat of a more detailed costing analysis, the use of a staff college would provide a cost effective alternative to external facilities.

The paper goes on to state *"several issues of principle upon which the success of a proposal to create a staff college will almost certainly hinge"*. These include:

- Location (particularly important for an All Wales commitment to be achieved)
- The amount and source of capital and start up costs
- The need for a business plan to ensure optimum utilisation with flexibility for external income generation

These points very much reflect the market and business oriented, at least theoretically and rhetorically, policy context of the period. The emphasis on cost effectiveness, income generation and entrepreneurialism are particularly notable as being from the language of this period. What we see in this is a shift which created many tensions from a centrally planned notion of a corporate NHS Wales to the introduction of a market emulating public service espousing business style principles. However, this is somewhat at odds with the planning and health gain perspectives of the WHPF and previous emphasis on the need for corporateness on an All Wales level.

This was to be further emphasised by the appointment of Conservative John Redwood to the post of Secretary of State for Wales in 1992. Redwood's appointment was seen, by some, as resulting in the promotion of a market oriented 'New Right' agenda in Wales. Prior to this Wales had been seen to lag somewhat behind England in implementing market based reforms such as the introduction of the internal market into the NHS. This was associated, by some, with the personalities occupying the Secretary of State for Wales role. John Redwood came to Wales with a clear commitment to both the ideology and policies of the New Right as espoused by Margaret Thatcher and Sir Keith Joseph in the UK and by Ronald Reagan in the United States. John Redwood was clearly committed to taking this experiment to Wales. This period, perhaps not coincidentally, also saw the end of John Wyn Owen's period as Director of the NHS in Wales and the disbanding of the WHPF and ultimately of the WHCSA.

Returning to the concept paper of September 1989, the issues of principle move to the more mundane:

- The required size and scope of educational, research and accommodation facilities
- Whether to build new or encompass existing facilities
- How the college would be staffed
- The urgency of the whole issue

The paper concludes with two elements of future action:

"The assessment of real commitment to the principle and use of a staff college by sufficient DHAs to make it effective. All DHAs together with a clear indication of weight of usage and likely subject matters.

A detailed cost benefit analysis encompassing "new build" and "re-use" options, location, core staffing, business planning, required facilities and the role of the college in relation to non NHS bodies"

The paper concludes that this study was to be completed by the end of 1989.

The early concepts of a staff college raise some important issues which were to be of significance both for the college itself and for the wider NHS in Wales. The genesis of the college is firmly rooted in emergent concepts of managerialism and its application to the NHS and indeed to the rest of the public sector. Differences in understandings over the language of training against that of development and of the concept of a more Fordist training centre predating the more cerebral notion of a college reflect different views regarding the ways in which health service managers and clinicians should be developed. The development of a new organisation such as the college also reflects the importance of locating any such change in the context of the dominant policy drivers of the time and of ensuring the agreement of key stakeholders across the health policy community. Moreover, the early thinking about the college reflects tensions regarding central and local roles and the development of a concept of a corporate NHS in Wales.

3

Moving from Idea to Reality

The Staff College story then moved from the concept paper stage to a key meeting of stakeholders in 1990 in the Heronston Hotel, Bridgend. The "Heronston Meeting" was an invited 'think tank' seminar facilitated by the consultancy firm Management Advisory Service (MAS). The invitees came from the Welsh Office, WHCSA and two Health Authorities. These included representatives from the nursing and medical professions but the meeting was dominated unsurprisingly by those with a management background. For a full list of the invitees see Appendix 1.

Following this MAS issued a report of the seminar. The report re-emphasised the need for a cohesive corporate vision for NHS Wales and stated:

"Such a task requires a corporate approach to health care combined with a mechanism which facilitates change in the organisational culture to make the culture receptive to corporateness".

This leads to an espoused purpose of the Staff College:

*   *"to be an instrument for change in health care services in Wales*
*   *to develop and promulgate a shared vision of health care in Wales".*

This raises a new strand of discussion in relation to the role of a Staff College – that through its activities in training, development and beyond it can actually impact on changing and improving services within the NHS. This has become an increasing preoccupation of the NHS, particularly in England, over recent years where modernisation and the continual improvement of health care services have come to dominate the health care agenda.

15

This new thread moves the proposed activities of a Staff College some way beyond that of the training centre of the Deloitte paper of 1984:

"A number of methods might be adopted to achieve these aims. Amongst them is the support a College could provide for research and development in health care, in organisational training and development; in providing support to managers and as a focal point for the cross fertilisation of ideas and their dissemination".

As part of this shift and located in the debate regarding thinking and training practice the document states:

"Thus the college will not be an orthodox training centre but a place for education, thinking, research, discussion and debate. It will be a meeting point, a place to congregate for sharing ideas and for intellectual stimulation".

Moreover the concept of the Staff College seemingly becomes something altogether more elitist than in its original inception:

"The college will cater for the needs of the NHS in Wales through the bringing together of Executive and Non Executive Directors, Clinical Directors and other Senior Staff... once the college becomes established it would be expected that it would become a pre-requisite for advancement that certain categories of staff would need to attend the College and participate in its activities.

In this way the College would become a stepping stone in career development, where those attending would become a part of a select group of attendees, creating an alumni of members, all of whom have contributed to the development of health care in Wales through the work of the College."

This document also saw the first references to a view that the Staff College might be involved in more than just health care:

"Whilst the emphasis is on health care, it would be the intention to attract to the College those concerned with social care"

As with modernisation in England this was to become a dominant theme for Welsh public policy particularly in the post devolution era with an emphasis on 'joined up' and in particular 'partnership' work-

ing. The paper also starts to deal with the very practical arrangements surrounding finance and accountabilities for the new college.

The key place of the Director of NHS Wales and those within his
inner circle in making some of these shifts is clear in the letter written by the Director to the Chairmen and District General Managers
of Health Authorities shortly after the Heronston Meeting in July
1990. This stated:

*"An essential purpose of a Staff College would be to create and
maintain a sense of common purpose in NHS Wales at a time when
the service itself was becoming more pluralistic and to act as an instrument of change for health care services in Wales and to promote a
shared vision throughout the principality".*

Here the vision and approach of the planning of corporate NHS
Wales can be seen to already be in some conflict with the more
pluralistic principles of the emergent, and ever more decentralised,
health care market. This is further reinforced in the letter:

*"The strategic intent and direction outlined in the work of the Welsh
Health Planning Forum issued by the Department last November, will
be the clear guiding force behind the activities of the College and
would encompass education, thinking, research, discussion and debate"*

and the more elitist approach:

*"The needs of top managers for provider services, clinical directors,
members of teams and boards in directly managed units will be ca-
tered for by the College providing a target audience of some 500-600
staff."*

The letter also echoes previous views of the role of NHS staff
within the college:

*"A major feature of the College's operation would be the use of
senior managers and professionals as 'faculty' members, ensuring
not only the maximum benefit from the extensive experience of such
staff but also providing personal development for the individuals concerned"*

This was a theme that would ultimately be picked up in the establishment of the Staff College 'Fellows'. The letter also identifies three

criteria by which the success of the college would be judged, notably the degree to which it:

- provided appropriate services, stimulus and focus for strategic change
- attracted quality staff and gained recognition for their work
- raised the standards of research and education in the health and social care field

Following this letter a reference group was set up and MAS engaged to take the practicalities of an option appraisal forward. However it is at this point that pushing the initiative forward appears to get somewhat 'stuck'. Whilst meetings of reference and steering groups take place, combined with option appraisals, this is at odds with a change both in the political and policy climate and in the role and commitment of some of the prime movers of the original staff college concept. This emphasises the importance of any new development converging with the dominant political and managerial agenda if it is to move from idea to inception.

A year after the Director's letter and the Heronston Meeting Stephen Prosser, then Director of the Manpower Services and NHS Wales based, in WHCSA, seeks to reinvigorate the proposal and the practical options for taking this forward. The paper sent to the Welsh Office to support this in 1991 reinforces the view that there was still *"widespread general support for a Staff College for Wales"*. The purpose of the College in this paper was somewhat amended from the Director's letter of the previous year:

- *"a place to think, discuss ideas, consider options and exchange views with colleagues.*
- *The centre for research to take forward the All Wales strategies*
- *To run development programmes for our senior staff, perhaps numbering 4-5,000 professionals*
- *A conference centre thereby reducing our extensive use of hotels*
- *Some linkage with the provision of professional/clinical education"*

The options ranged from NHS Wales buying a property outright, public private partnerships, a partnership with England through to the College acting as a purchasing organisation with a small staff. The last option was very much in keeping with the concepts of purchaser and provider split underpinned by the internal market. However, both this and the first option of outright ownership were ruled out in the option appraisal undertaken by MAS. However it was stated that the purchaser organisation option might be a useful interim measure and a means of kick starting the project.

At the same time as these developments, and in line with the issue of links between academia and practice, a proposal to establish a Chair in Health Service Management emerged. Promoted by one of the protagonists of the Heronston Meeting the proposal stated that in order *"to facilitate and accelerate the development of Health Service Management research, education and training within Wales"* the Chair should be created. It was suggested that this be established at Cardiff Business School and that the person appointed would be the founding director of the staff college. In discussing the college the paper states:

"It is clear that such a role can only be performed in close collaboration with all parts of the Higher Education Sector within Wales"

The issue of location of the college also emerges within this paper with a suggestion that the college could be provided within a proposed, but as yet never built, postgraduate Business School in Cardiff Bay.

The rationale for the Chair was:

"The present rapid rate of change in the management and organization of the Health Service increases the need and urgency for this to be done. By creating a Chair in this area a great deal could be done to ensure both academic leadership and the co-ordination of activities within the Health Service and the Education sector"

It was stated in 1991 that *"the college would concentrate on operational policy research... pure policy research would be undertaken through the Chair"*. It was intended that by 1992 that there would be a joint appointment to the Chair in Health Services Management and Director of the Staff College and although this had not been achieved it was still stated as an intention in July 1992. However, funding for the academic post was a recurring problem which would ultimately preclude its development. By 1992 the Steering Group had decided, in a switch from the Business School, that the Chair would be located in the University of Wales College of Medicine, possibly within the proposed Institute of Public Health, and would be Director or Head of an Academic Board within the Staff College. As funding issues, driven by the on-going inability to find a sponsor, continued to frustrate the development of a Chair it was ultimately proposed that in order to avoid delays in setting up the college the Director could become a Visiting Professor. This was the model finally followed although the desire to create a Chair in Health Service Management within a university in Wales never completely disappeared.

At the same time as the Staff College concept was under discussion in NHS Wales there were also similar discussions going on in England. Interestingly these discussions drew in part from Welsh ideas, thinking and progress and there was a level of cross fertilisation of ideas and knowledge, in particular gleaned from visits to other management colleges in the public and private sectors.

By the early 1990s the concept of a Staff College had become locked into what is a not unfamiliar round of bureaucracy of report writing and meetings. This reflects the progress of many innovative developments within the context of the NHS and public services. The forces of bureaucracy and the requirement both to produce a paper audit trail and gain the agreement of a range of stakeholders, is often at odds with attempting to make changes or progress innovative developments within a relatively short timescale.

This reflects a tension in the brief given to MAS in their task for progressing the concept of a Staff College. At points there was a lack of clarity in identifying the purpose of the future college between those who viewed it as a 'Gentleman's Club' with a more elitist role and those who viewed it as a 'Working Men's Club' that would cover a much wider range of people within the NHS. The concept of the Staff College was also at this point lacking a 'heavyweight champion' in both the NHS and the Welsh Office to turn the various ideas regarding the college into action.

In a 1990 MAS paper a somewhat different version of the purpose of the Staff College emerged from that of previous reports and meetings:

- Focal point of health (and social service) staff in a pluralist NHS
- Co-ordinating agency of organisational development and change; to assist in implementing white papers
- Instrument of the Welsh Office in bringing about change and implementing policy

- Educational institution drawing the educational facilities of other agencies
- Training establishment providing facilities for the training of a broad cross section of NHS (and social services) staff
- Focal point for the provision of cerebral relief for NHS (and social services) staff
- Co-ordinating agency, stimulant and participant in health and social research
- Centre for health (and social) care, research, development, education and training

The role of the Staff College as an instrument of government policy was a new one and one which would ultimately cause many tensions in the future, particularly in the advent of devolution.

One other reason for the stasis in development of the Staff College was the need for convergence between the policy environment and the idea. At this point the corporate centralist notion of the Staff College was increasingly at odds with the market driven environment that was emerging throughout the NHS.

Two models of operation also emerged in the 1990 MAS report:

Model 1
- A college which would be a forum for All Wales meetings of various kinds
- A think tank/research organisation
- An influence on policy and strategy within the NHS and beyond
- A consultancy
- Co-ordinator of initiatives
- Vehicle for organisational and attitudinal change
- Organisation at the cutting edge of development
- Organisation undertaking quality assurance assessment
- Organisation involved in management arbitration

Model 2
- Organisation which co-ordinates management training
- Organisation provides facilities for training conducted by others
- Organisation which is cutting edge for management training
- Accrediting bids for management training
- Organisation which identifies next generations of managers and trains them

Whilst there could be a combination of these options this report indicated greater support for the second model given *"a clear opinion about the need for improvement in the management training arrangements in Wales"*. What also emerges at this point is the thorny issue of funding with a view emerging that neither model is worth investing in and a downright rejection of top slicing.

A 1990 MAS document suggested the mission for the college and services which could be provided to achieve this mission:

Mission	Services
Improve care for patients and clients through improved management	Draws together managers for the purpose of pursuing discussion, analysis and debate
To be a stimulant for desired change in health care in Wales	Providing consultancy advice to the health service
To provide an independent source of thinking, research and development in health care	A facility which embraces within it some existing services such as the Welsh Health Planning Forum
To contribute to the development of policies and strategies for health care	A facility which may be used to accommodate training programmes
	Researches and analyses issues for the health service
	Organises and controls management training for health services managers
	A facility which accommodates and arranges seminars and workshops on relevant issues

The policy dimension was also new and potentially one which cast the college more in the role of 'think tank'.

Whilst at this point the college as a physical entity is not entirely a 'given' the options regarding physical attributes and location occupy much of the business case. Moreover within the context of 'Working for Patients' it is proposed that the Staff College be developed as an NHS Trust in its own right.

The MAS Business Plan for the Staff College of 1991 shows a strong link to the 1990 document but refines the objectives and other factors following comments from stakeholders. The plan strongly reflects the mission of the 1990 plan with services refined into four groupings under the following headings:

- Core Services: library, research, independent thinking, dissemination
- Development and training services
- Consultancy
- Hire/use of facilities

These services specifically include:

- Facilities and services to attract people from any professional background who wish to engage in short or long term research or project work
- A facility for discussion, analysis and debate
- Consultancy advice primarily to the health service
- Co-ordination and provision of training and development activities and the management of some national programmes
- A library and information resource
- Facilities for seminars, workshops and conferences
- Human resource planning and skills analysis

In the MAS Marketing Strategy "The Target Image" for the College is described as:

- The "Ideas House"
- The place for healthcare research
- The forum for the NHS in Wales
- An international healthcare forum
- Attendance at the Staff College is a career move
- People focused activities
- Improving patient care

Shortly after this MAS and the NHS part company reflecting the tensions and difficulties in pursuing the Staff College concept over a number of years. As stated by the subsequent "Staff College Project Review" of June 1992 the notion of setting up a Staff College had been debated for a number of years. The Review stated that by 1990 this had been given greater impetus when a consultancy contract was let to develop the role and a proposal for a practical realisation of a college. Whilst there was general agreement regarding the need to establish a college the practical proposals were rejected in 1991 as unrealistic and excessive both in terms of scope and cost.

The period also saw the emergence of a discussion regarding the links between the academic world and training and development in the NHS. The links between academia and practice were ones which were to challenge both organisations. The research and theoretically driven world of academia was often seen as being of little relevance to the 'hands on' firefighting world of the NHS manager engaged as he or she was with day to day matters of service delivery. However, it was recognised that creating a Chair in Health Services Management would develop and give credibility to a new academic discipline which would seek to bridge the gap between the two worlds. As will be seen, the notion of providing an evidence base for policy, management, organisation development and leadership was eventually to become a dominant driver for the NHS in the late 1990s.

The difficulties of moving the idea of a staff college to actually establishing the college dominated this period. Those seeking to move the college idea forward at this point were using techniques of report writing, meetings and option appraisal that were more familiar in the NHS predating the introduction of the internal market. The more market and business driven ethos of the new NHS suggested a more entrepreneurial and less bureaucratic approach and, as will be seen, this was the approach that was to bear fruit. Moreover, the period saw the gradual development of the internal market and the emergence of NHS Trusts as providers of healthcare services and Health Authorities, which had previously been the pre-eminent organisation within NHS Wales, as purchasers of healthcare. This made gaining commitment from within the NHS Wales family a more difficult consideration. NHS Trusts were encouraged to work in a decentralised and autonomous way with previous command and control models from Health Authority down to Units of Management swept away. NHS Trusts were keen to embrace their new powers and responsibilities and were less willing to consider centralist initiatives and there were very many more organisations which now had to be included in any discussion. The need to gain commitment from the range of NHS stakeholders as well as from government was one which was to challenge the college throughout its existence.

4

The 'Ipso Facto' Staff College

Following the departure of MAS the work of the steering group and the appointment of a Project Manager can be seen in driving the development of the college. In 1992 it was suggested that a 'Phase 1' college be created which would draw together existing activities. Links with UWCM were seen as key in order to:

- Overlap management and medical training
- Encourage participation of clinicians in management processes and ongoing development
- Enhance general managers awareness of the medical perspective
- Benefit from shared training and residential facilities

The desire to bring clinicians into the management fold drew from a clear policy directive based on a view that clinicians, in particular doctors, were key in achieving efficiency within the NHS as the main allocators of resources at a grass roots level. The engagement of clinicians as part of early staff college thinking was, however, something which was to be a distinctive element of the staff college.

It was also interesting to note that at this point the steering group still favoured a *"club type ambience that would serve to encourage a sense of belonging and commitment to an NHS Wales culture...."* This view of a 'gentleman's club' which would encourage new ways of thinking amongst something of an NHS managerial elite was not however something that would ultimately gain favour.

The role of the college at this point was articulated as
- Developing overall NHS culture
- Management development in all its aspects
- Research and Development on current operational issues
- Development and co-ordination of collective initiatives
- Development of new ideas

The college was to be a major contributor but not an exclusive provider and would be responsive not directive. This reflected the early tensions between central and local roles and a desire that the college was firmly rooted in the values, workings and requirements of the NHS. Gaining support from within the NHS, particularly amongst managers and clinicians, was critical although it could not outweigh the need to get political and civil servant commitment.

The Steering Group had identified the following ingredients of a staff college:

- The appointment of a Chair in Health Services Management as an essential prerequisite
- Small scale phased development possibly within a Cardiff hotel location
- A full college to follow in 2-3 years in close proximity to the postgraduate medical school

The appointment of the Project Manager was driven by a desire to get an 'outsider' to push the project forwards, given the difficulties that had previously been experienced. The appointment was an individual from outside the NHS with entrepreneurial flair and a 'self made millionaire'. This allowed him to ask different and brutally honest questions and to judge the answers against a business oriented template. This was, however, somewhat at odds with the prevailing NHS culture even with the creation of decentralised NHS Trusts.

The Project Manager demonstrated his different perspective in his "Proposal to form an NHS Wales Staff College". This sought to locate the College within the dominant Redwood authored policy document of the period "Caring for the Future" and states that the college should be set up from April 1993. At this point the notion of a 'Learning Organisation' permeates the discussion as demonstrated in the newly formulated mission statement:

"To facilitate the development of a 'Learning Organisation' culture throughout NHS Wales and within that cultural framework to facilitate the continuous development of the individuals and organisations that make up NHS Wales so that separately and collectively they might contribute more effectively to achieving the Strategic Intent and Direction of NHS Wales"

However the concept of a Learning Organisation is not without debate and by February 1994 the minutes of the Staff College Development Group identified that no common understanding of learning organisation culture had been established and that it was felt that the label could in fact generate hostility within the NHS itself. It is interesting, however, to note how concepts of the learning organisation and methods which can underpin this, have increasingly come to be accepted by those working within healthcare and other organisations.

The process had, however, moved to forming a college 'ipso facto' at Hensol Castle (an NHS property that continued also to care for those with learning disabilities) with the Welsh Office and NHS Wales as joint founders to ensure ownership. The college would thus undertake existing activities which could 'sensibly' come under the remit – much of this reflects the tensions between central direction and local provision. The college would undertake new activities *"arising out of the OD review, Caring for the Future and the implementation of the NHS reforms"*. In the longer term the college was seen as potentially undertaking operational research. Links with academia were cast in broader terms than previously although mindful of the potential to develop the Chair in Health Services Management. The criteria for success were rather different from those of previous years reflecting a clear drive to get the major stakeholders 'on board':

- Active commitment of the founders
- Demonstrate financial independence within 2 years
- Emergence of a strong 'learning organisation' culture becoming evident within NHS Wales as a whole within 18 months of inception
- Growth of fully funded requested activities
- Level of participation by clinicians
- Level and growth of services provided to other organisations

The period was also marked by a number of discussions around the location of the college, the status and funding arrangements and some frustration on the part of the project manager who at one point states *"that nothing practical has happened towards the inception of a Staff College"*.

A target of September 1993 was set for the establishment of the college and the potentially 'international' dimension of the college was also raised. At a subsequent meeting to discuss this report the concept of founders was to be further progressed by the Director of NHS Wales asking Chairs and Chief Executives to support the venture and pay a subscription 'joining' or 'founder' fee. A letter was sent to ask NHS organisations to join the foundation of the college and to contribute £3,000 each together with the establishment of a 'task force' to take forward the proposals. This reflects the concerns that the staff college could be seen as a top down directive closely associated with the Director of NHS Wales. As has been discussed, a centrally managed college was at odds with the rhetoric of the increasingly devolved management arrangements of the early 1990s. Having NHS organisations as founders and funders was seen as a way around this. This consortium approach was seen to fall out of an ongoing organisational review rather than an isolated initiative.

Thus by 1993 three key elements were in place:

- Formal foundation activities
- Development of an initial college programme
- Establishment of an administrative framework

At this point a former Health Authority District General Manager, was seconded to the Welsh Office and then established as the Staff College Project Director. The Summary Progress report produced for the College at this point states that the aim of the College was *"to be the largest single influence in the development of Leaders, Organisations and an overall culture which will ensure that the NHS Wales can achieve its goal of securing levels of health of the population of Wales which are comparable with the best in Europe by the year 2000"*. This was still echoing the words of the Strategic Intent and Direction as well as combining it with wider understandings of leadership. The activities of the College were summarised as:

- Designing and implementing a Leadership Development Programme
- Undertaking high level OD activity
- Acting as the main source of advice and impetus for evolution of Learning Culture within Wales
- Contributing extensively to the development aspect of Research and Development function in Wales
- Providing a conduit for the intellect of the operational wing of the NHS to contribute to the overall vision and strategy adopted for the service
- Consultancy
- Acting as a problem-solving agent for medium or long-term problems through facilitating key learning networks

- Directly providing some of the learning requirements which cannot satisfactorily accommodated through existing agencies

It was suggested that the College initially conduct ad hoc activities with the first priority a 'catch up' exercise concerned with clinicians in management. The College was also to pick up key major contemporary topics with the first priority Corporate Governance for Chairs, Non Executive and Executive Board members.

Reflecting the protected positions of other existing organisations within NHS Wales, the Summary Report states the need to avoid duplication and establish a 'niche' for the college. This is suggested to lie around issues of health policy and strategy, strategic aspects of leadership and a broader public sector approach to leadership development. It is stated that there will be two distinct parts of the college – business and academic. The quest to find the appropriate level and range of activities for the college would challenge the College throughout its existence. Whilst much attention was paid at this stage to planning out and identifying these activities, as will be seen, many of them ultimately emerged on an ad hoc basis.

The Business Development Plan for the College calls for *"an organisation that is positioned at the crossroads of the operational and developmental wings of NHS Wales; has an independent status and is 'owned' by the service as a whole. In addition the key criterion for success is that the college should become fully self-financing within 5 years of inception"*. The activities are summarised as:

- Supporting development of a collaborative common culture
- Supporting the development of leadership and management skills within the healthcare sector
- Providing a forum for the interchange of ideas about future development of the healthcare sector within Wales
- Carrying out and disseminating research

The Plan goes on to state:

"The Staff College for NHS Wales is an exciting and innovative concept... It will respond flexibly and imaginatively to enable staff within NHS Wales to:
- *Learn from their peers*
- *Network with other organisations*
- *Stop re-inventing the wheel*
- *Establish and learn from best practices*

... The style and culture of the college will be based on:
- *Listening*
- *Anticipating and responding*
- *Providing continuity and order in a fast changing world*
- *Generating, debating and evaluating ideas about the development of healthcare in Wales*

Above all else it will be the agent of change which will help NHS Wales to become the learning organisation."

The mission of the college is espoused as *"To foster the development of a 'learning organisation' culture throughout NHS Wales and within that framework to play a lead role in the development of individuals and organisations so that collectively and separately and in partnership with related organisations, they may achieve the strategy objectives of NHS Wales"* and the key objectives of the college are:

- NHS Wales Culture Change (focused on the Learning Culture)
- Leadership (managerial and professional)
- Organisation Development
- Ad-hoc including management development of clinicians

These objectives bring together the range of activities that have developed through the emergence of the concept of a staff college. They are, however, somewhat updated in the light of the dominant language of the time including an emphasis on leadership and changing culture. The emphasis is both on individual and organisational interventions to effect change within the NHS. The plan recognises the college is an embryonic organisation and must concentrate its limited resources on key areas *"where it can make a unique contribution"*. It recognises that there are many activities well provided for by other organisations – the college is to seek to make constructive links with these bodies and only what cannot be provided for by commissioning and networking would be provided directly.

It is interesting to note at this point that measuring both outputs and outcomes for the college become important and in line with requirements being increasingly placed on the NHS. Thus the Staff College has to articulate those factors that will demonstrate its success. The success factors for the college were identified as:

- Recognition of the Staff College by NHS Wales as an organisation of influence and excellence in fields of leadership, change and cultural development

- Distinctive improvement in management capacity in NHS Wales
- Identification of the next generation of leaders
- Staff developed in Wales filling leadership roles elsewhere
- Wales regarded as an attractive place to work because of its approach to leadership and management development
- A distinctive shift measured using the appropriate audit tools towards the 'Learning Organisation' culture
- Doctors, nurses and other professionals consider the college as the natural place to develop their management skills

It is suggested that the Welsh Office will underwrite core development costs with the option of Independent Charitable Foundation status still favoured. The concept of a company limited by guarantee was also explored as was the option of a consortium of NHS Trusts, Health Authorities and others. Offices were established in Hensol and North Wales but there were continued difficulties in agreeing the status and funding for the College and therefore in actually launching it. In part this reflects the restrictions that existed at that time on public service organisational forms which made more radical solutions such as charitable or company status difficult. Alternative organisational forms also raised important questions for the accountability and responsiveness of any such organisation which ultimately would still be funded from the public purse. However, an organisation such as the Staff College did not lie easily within the existing organisations of the NHS – NHS Trusts or Health Authorities - nor was it appropriate for the organisation to lie within the Welsh Office. This lack of overall 'organisational fit' was to be an ongoing challenge for the College.

The options for legal status and the continued debate regarding the relationship with the University of Wales also continued to dog the development of the College through 1993 and into 1994. This reflects differences even within public sector organisations in terms of accountability and financial arrangements that make partnership working problematic. As an interim measure it is suggested that an NHS partner organisation is selected to provide for legal status and governance issues for the college with a long term objective stated as management by the University of Wales. In May 1994 it is suggested that the initial organisational structure of the college will be a Governing Council, Executive Board and Managing Trust. "The financing of the college is 'pump primed' initially by the Welsh Office. The Welsh Office proposes progressively to repatriate such funding to Authorities and Trusts and it will eventually be for Authorities and Trusts to determine whether they value the work of the college sufficiently to continue to financially support the services provided." Funding was to continue to be an issue given the devolved nature of health services funding following the introduction of the internal market. This created issues surrounding the 'top slicing' of monies by the Welsh Office and the alternative of collaborative arrangements for funding from each of the somewhat disparate organisations of the NHS in Wales.

An early offering of the 'ipso facto' Staff College was a 'Leadership Development Process'. This reflects the emerging preoccupation with the notion of leadership which could be seen to span both clinicians and managers and indeed to be a term which the former were comfortable with. However, there is some debate regarding how far the words manager and leader were used interchangeably in a way that perhaps the words administrator and manager had been used in the past. The Staff College was, however, to play a part in promoting emerging concepts of leadership, for example in its research on the notion and applicability of transformational leadership. At this stage Leadership was defined as:

"Leadership as a concept is significantly different from the notion of high level technical managerial competence which has characterised management development approaches in the past... change, vision, anticipation, innovation, risk and a greater concern with an active shaping of the future. Leaders also engage in a restless and continuous pursuit of a higher mission".

A Leadership Development Group was established to identify a leadership development process for NHS Wales. It was faced with two options – one was to think through the various options thoroughly and carefully and the other was to take a pragmatic approach and pilot an approach. Given the difficulties in launching and establishing any outputs for the college in this period it is unsurprising that the latter option was favoured. The following component parts of the process were identified:

- The use of existing performance review systems to identify high potential people to join existing leaders on a programme
- Design and introduction of a Development Centre approach through to Personal Development Plans (PDPs) for all on the leadership programme
- Work through with employers and individuals the practical implications of PDPs

- Continuous re-evaluation of philosophies and values

In line with the pragmatic approach an evolutionary and incremental line was taken with the Development Centre as the first stage.

The objectives of the Leadership Programme were identified as:
- Commissioning and providing general and personally tailored support to existing leaders
- Providing structures and processes for identifying next generations of leaders
- Devising a framework by which Leadership Development could proceed as a nationally orchestrated activity
- Commissioning, providing or shaping a broad range of educational, training and development opportunities

The Staff College would assemble a 'basket' of approved training and educational opportunities to achieve this including:
- Full leadership programmes
- Action programmes
- Masters, diploma programmes
- Short courses
- Seminars/workshops
- Skills programmes
- Key learning networks
- International programmes

The early 1990s witnessed the difficulties the Staff College had in moving from an idea to a reality. Debates regarding status, funding and functions continued to challenge its development as new organisational and policy arrangements came into force. The concept of a college did, however, have sufficient support to emerge in embryonic form taking a more pragmatic approach to creating a place for the college. Leadership development for both managers and clinicians was focused upon as a key area of activity for the 'ipso facto' Staff College. The position of the College was, however, by no means assured and it was debatable whether the new organisation would be stifled at birth.

5

Goodbye Old College...
Hello New College

The leadership development process was one of the few outputs of an embryonic organisation that was still struggling to be born. The Staff College was facing a serious crisis of confidence which resulted in a referendum of Chief Executives (which resulted in 11 for, 9 against, 1 undecided and 3 non returns). This reflected a number of factors and tensions surrounding the creation of the college. In part this related to frustration over the slow development of the college and limited outputs. It also reflected concerns regarding the 'ownership' of the college, its location and role within the NHS and its 'fitness for purpose'.

Stephen Prosser (then Managing Director of the Organisation Development Group which encompassed Manpower Consultancy Services) was asked by the Welsh Office to explore models of delivering the Staff College agenda in a bid to move the debate forwards. At the same time it became clear that Manpower Consultancy Services, which had some overlapping functions to the Staff College would, in line with political diktat regarding the future of WHCSA, not be retained. MCS and WHCSA were ultimately disbanded following John Redwood's direction and, in keeping with the Service's desire to devolve operational activity to the local level. The overlapping functions of MCS and the Staff College would prove fortuitous by ultimately providing a lever by which support could be gained for the Staff College by expediting the closure of MCS.

The proposal for the 'new' Staff College proposed the following key roles:

- "A Time to Think" – creating events which met the needs of Trusts and Health Authorities
- Research work – highly relevant and applied
- Development Programmes
- Conferences
- Consultancy

The need for a reborn organisation was emphasised: *"The Staff College can succeed but it needs to be recreated in the minds of people"*.

These discussions resulted in a new proposal for the Staff College which was to:

- Work with the service to identify need
- Work with providers to deliver tailored products
- Manage programmes
- Manage overall (development) processes

The products of the College were anticipated as including leadership, clinicians in management, organisational change, health policy issues and board development. It was felt that the college should focus on its products rather than on itself as an entity. This was something of a break with the approaches of the past. A different approach to progressing the establishment of the college was now emerging with the emphasis on decentralisation, reflecting the concerns of the NHS regarding central control over training and development. Consultation also became more important as a means of establishing the college, as an alternative approach to the more centralised methods previously used. This was also more in tune with the entrepreneurial climate of the market oriented NHS. The approach also recognised the need to engage individuals in order to ensure a level of personal support for the College that would carry it through. This did not focus on the lengthy meetings, reports and option appraisals of the previous era but in many ways adopted the 'back of the envelope' approach which allowed for quick and flexible movement.

By this time the NHS in Wales had a new director who concurred with the view that the college needed to be seen to be owned by the NHS in Wales; that the current arrangements for the 'old' college should be wound up and the new proposal accepted and developed. A chair for the management board was nominated and the 'old' college would come to an end on 31st December and the new college start on 1st January 1995 with a new Chief Executive in Stephen Prosser. This was to be combined with the role played by the Chair of the Management Group, Paul Williams, who commanded great respect within NHS Wales and possessed a commitment to learning and development. From this point onwards the proposal took on a momentum which reflected its pragmatism, the role of a champion and the convergence of this proposal, in comparison with those which had preceded it, with the current policy and organisational environment. It also provided an opportunity both to resolve the issues of the old staff college and accommodate some of the staff from the now defunct MCS. .

Core costs would be transferred from the Welsh Office on a ring-fenced basis for a three year period and this was mainly to cover the costs of five members of staff drawn from MCS. Thereafter funds would go to Health Authorities on a weighted capitation basis with the intention that Health Authorities would then fund the College. The new college was to have a high level advisory board and management group. The college would work towards developing a formal link with a university. An office would be created at Morriston Hospital, Swansea in addition to the small existing office in Wrexham thereby attempting to reconcile some of the issues regarding a South Wales focus for the college. It was agreed that Morriston Hospital NHS Trust would employ the College's staff. Thus the college would be an incorporated part of the NHS thereby removing the barriers of organisational form that had proved so problematic in previous years. Thus the issues of funding, location and 'ownership' were dealt with, at least on a temporary basis, by a number of relatively swift and pragmatic measures.

An extensive period of iterative consultation then followed in which many stakeholders were engaged to establish commitment. This involved presentations being delivered to a range of organisations across Wales. Well over 100 presentations were given which also sought to gather information about the needs of the service and how a College could deliver against these. Delivering against an NHS determined agenda and the clear location of the college within the NHS, albeit with links to the Welsh Office, was emphasised. This was to be critical in developing the new College. To succeed, it was perceived that the College should have a service led strategy which established what the service needed, who could provide it and, most importantly of all, how it could best be made to happen.

The concept of fellows also emerged at this point, through which senior health services managers in Wales provided expertise and support across the range of College work, most notably development programmes. This was an important development in gaining support for and involvement in the college from a range of key stakeholders within NHS Wales. It also provided the opportunity for these individuals to pursue their own development and to ensure that College work reflected and was grounded in NHS practice.

In December of 1994 a letter was sent out to formally launch the new college:

"I am pleased to inform you that the Staff College will come fully into operation on the 1ˢᵗ January 1995... The Staff College will work with the Service to identify and meet, wherever possible, the individual and organisational development needs of clinical, managerial and other staff. It will not duplicate activities being undertaken by others".

The inception and early months of the college were marked by discussions and disagreements regarding the funding of the college which were to have longer term implications for the stability of the college. However by 1996 a formal Service Level Agreement (SLA) was signed between the college and the Welsh Office which gives an indication of the activities of the college:

- Leadership and Clinicians in Management
- Change Management
- Opportunity 2000 (related to the equal opportunities agenda)

And in the 1997/8 SLA the activities had expanded to:

- Nurse Management Development Programmes
- Clinicians in Management
- Primary Healthcare
- Primary Healthcare Certificate/Diploma/Masters
- Chief Executive Programme
- Executive Director Programme
- Middle Managers Programme
- Development Scholarship
- 10ᵗʰ Anniversary Seminars
- Board Development
- Clinical Team Development
- Alumni Association
- Opportunity 2000

These early developments give an indication of the preoccupations of the NHS of the day. The engagement of clinicians, in particular doctors and nurses, was a constant theme of the college from its inception. The emergence of primary care as a key area for both individual and organisation development was one which was linked to an emerging view that the NHS needed to be 'primary care led'. Change management was an underpinning theme of many programmes and activities. This reflected early discussions regarding the role of the College as a change agent and an increasing interest in ways in which a large organisation such as the NHS could change and what levers could be used to achieve this. It also reflected a growing body of academic and applied research and theory generation on the theme of change management.

In 1997 John Wyn Owen, who had left Wales to lead the New South Wales health service and who subsequently left Sydney to head up the Nuffield Trust in London, gave a speech to the International Hospital Foundation in Melbourne entitled *"Staff Colleges – Their Role in the Modern Health Care World"* which drew on his experiences in Wales and New South Wales, Australia. This speech sums up some of the main issues that surrounded the creation and establishment of the Staff College. Wyn Owen based staff development in a period of unprecedented change on principles of organisational learning. Key stakeholders and traditional tools of implementation were used to establish the colleges and in Wales it was recognised that this was initially a frustrating process. As a result of consultation a clear set of principles and values were adopted for this college without walls, a virtual organisation which rather than investing in buildings and faculty would commission others and would:

- Absorb lessons from elsewhere
- Work with people in the service and develop Fellows
- Enable doctors and managers to learn together
- Remember primary care and avoid being monopolised by secondary care
- Emphasise the family of health especially in an increasingly decentralised service

Developments in old and new Wales were, according to Wyn Owen, based on similar concepts:
- A total continuous learning process through which managers developed their competency;
- variety of formal, informal, structured and unstructured learning experiences
- self development through programmes.

John Wyn Owen expressed the view that there was a need for more health specific development resources to be in touch with community ideas whose culture is able to meet community needs oriented towards evidence based decisions and practice. This required professional staff and managers to be brought together with programmes that were locally relevant drawing on international best practice. Wyn Owen, obviously proud of his contribution to the creation of the two colleges, concluded:

"The development of a staff college is not a replacement for other educational sectors and professional development programmes, rather it is a finishing school that provides the key values associated with running the health systems – to be shared and developed".

6

Funding the New College

The issue of funding was one that would be a source of discussion as the Staff College developed reflecting the discussions held prior to its establishment. Funding is key, not merely because it provides the financial resources through which objectives can be achieved, but as an indication of policy priorities and organisational imperatives. The entrepreneurial approach which led to the establishment of the new college provided for a flexible base in funding which had both advantages and disadvantages. Positively it allowed the organisation to work more responsively and take on work to meet emerging priorities. Negatively it made for a constant struggle to assure a solid foundation for the college, particularly in respect to funding its staffing establishment.

In 1995 £241k recurrent funding was made available for staff plus overheads which left a shortfall which the Staff College was to meet with consultancy work. This initiated an ongoing debate regarding 'core' work (funded by the NHS directly) and non core work which included courses which were directly charged for and consultancy. The division between these two types of activity would continue to be problematic in financial and contractual discussions. In many ways the split between the activities was somewhat artificial and historic with a number of development programmes, some of which had existed prior to the establishment of the college, providing the bedrock of college funding.

In 1999 a Programme and Review Group was established by the College's Management Group to review programmes and projects. The review encouraged the Staff College to further involve the NHS in the development of its business plans and to increase its activities in outcome based evaluation. It also recognised that although delivering programmes and projects was one part of the college's range of activities there was support for greater involvement of the college in strategic and organisation development issues across the NHS. The review proposed that £1.3 million should be made available per annum for programmes, in particular All Wales Schemes such as the

Management Development Scheme and Specialist Registrars programme. This reflected an emphasis on graduate management development and management development for clinicians. £300k was to be made available for development costs and £500K would be provided for staff and overhead costs. Some costs were to be paid for directly by course participants and their organisations.

The funding of the college also raised issues of who was actually the customer in the post internal market world. Health Authorities had had training resources devolved to them and there was much debate regarding how much should be repatriated to the Staff College. In 1999 the Health Authorities recommended that a £2.1million core budget should be funded and guaranteed for three years and that further funding should come through consultancy and direct charging. The need to establish longer term core funding for staff and overheads at the college was a pressing issue. The funding of the Staff College was to be agreed by Chief Executives throughout Wales in accordance with business plans produced by the college.

The debate regarding core and non core activities also led the college to develop and review its pricing policy. The college was expected to earn income to meet its full running costs. There was no charge for externally funded programmes; for special events there was a variable mark up and consultancy was costed at £500 a day (or £600 for the Chief Executive). This was organisational rather than personal consultancy work and was reinvested into the College. However, it was identified that there was tension between building up consultancy and delivering on the core agenda.

The Annual Reports produced by the Staff College provide an interesting history of the growth in and application of funding:

1997	
Staffing:	250,000
Operating:	98,800
Accommodation:	29,650
Total:	378,450
Managed through:	
Schemes:	580,000
Organisational Development	218,000
SPRs	37,100
Primary Care	7,600
Total	842,700

1998	
Staff Costs (core)	203,000
Staff Costs (schemes)	151,000
Operating costs	134,000
Accommodation	32,600
Total	520,600
Managed through:	
All Wales Schemes	770,000
Organisational Development	160,000
Primary Care	18,300

By 1999 the report adopts a different format in presenting the funding with schemes directly included into general funding rather than represented separately. This reflects a view that this was an integral part of the College's work.

1999	
Core Costs and Overheads	514,000
Deliver all schemes	1,337,000
New projects and developments	308,000
Total:	2,159,000
All Wales Schemes:	
MDS	460,000
Financial Management and Accountancy	504,000
Leaders from Within	52,000
Nurse Management Development Scheme	103,000
Widening Horizons	84,000
Specialist Registrars	134,000
Total:	1,337,000

By 2000 funding is represented very differently with the allocation from the NHS in Wales performing the core element of the College's funding and additional income made up from trading activities and from reserves that the College had built up. It is interesting to note that the report does not identify how far this covers the actual running costs of the College.

2000	
Allocation from NHS Wales:	2.202m
Trading Income	0.322m
Development Reserves	0.386m
Efficiency Savings	0.200m
Total	3.110m

The history of the funding of the College demonstrates the growth in the funding for the college, which reflects a wider and greater range of activities, combined with increased operating costs. This can be seen in the college growing from just 5 staff at its inception to some 60 by 2001, with a turnover of some £3.7 million, together with a range of associates and contractors who contributed to the delivery of schemes and other activities. It is interesting to explore why the College grew so quickly and across such a wide range of activities. In part this must be attributed to the success of the College in delivering its products. This gained the confidence of those using and paying for services which meant in turn that the College was used more and more and developed increasingly diverse activities. Moreover, although the College had initially considered acting primarily as a commissioning organisation this was seen to be easier in theory than practice. The time spent in writing specifications and monitoring and developing these with a limited range of providers were outweighed by the advantages of providing services internally and this was evidenced in the development of a number of programmes, particularly those for clinicians.

This also made the College an attractive place for NHS staff to come and work within. The College started to attract creative individuals who were keen to 'grow' new roles for example in research and learning technology. More staff were also required to work on the increasing range of internally provided activities. The growth of the College was not without its challenges. It is often assumed that organisations grow hierarchically and in a straight line. This was not the case with the College whose structure was perhaps more akin to those seen in creative organisations such as advertising agencies. The growth in staff led to some breakdowns in infrastructure and, given the College's place within the accountabilities of the NHS, a requirement to make a step change to introducing stronger systems and mechanisms to manage the organisation. The development of a robust project management regime, as adopted in similar organisations outside the NHS, might have provided some solutions, had this been initiated from the outset. There was however an inherent tension in this change – the need to create the apparatus of a larger organisation was at odds with a more flexible organisational structure. This was a key challenge for this type of organisation and the search for appropriate accountability and infrastructure arrangements is one that is not easily resolved.

7

Staff College Activities

The College produced a number of business plans which identified both past achievements and future aspirations. These also provide an interesting insight into the political, policy and managerial context within which management and leadership development was emerging. As an example *"Building on Current Strategies to Meet New Circumstances – Business Plan 1998-2001"* was based on four factors:

- Planning and Priorities Guidance for NHS Wales 1998-1999 circulated by the Welsh Office. Government objectives which were now part of the ethos of 'New Labour', which had come to power in 1997, included *"improving the public's health"*, *"partnership not competition"*, *"high standards of care and high quality of service"*, *"response to its patients and to the communities it serves"*. A new strategic framework for NHS Wales was emerging. At the same time education, training and professional development was claimed as *"the policy context which provides the greatest opportunity and influence upon the work of the Staff College"*
- *"Putting Patients First"*, which was published in 1998, was the Welsh version of the 1997 English White Paper *"A New NHS Modern and Dependable"* which heralded New Labour's vision of the NHS. Putting Patients First contained a range of commitments concerned with personal development and organisational change. This included education and training; organisational development; lifelong learning; team working; cross boundary collaboration; board development; primary care development; human resource management; re-emergence of PEOPLE principles; management development
- Lifelong Learning: taken from the Green Paper *"Learning is for Everyone"*
- The Service Review: Welsh Health Authorities and Trusts had commissioned and published a far-reaching investigation into the supply and demand for health services in Wales

In addition activities were to be related to the "Putting People First" human resource development agenda. The College was therefore to be 'People Centred' with effective people policies articulated through recruitment, retention and development, contractual arrangements, team structures and staffing levels.

These factors reflect a clear attempt by the Staff College to locate itself within the dominant policy paradigm of the moment. This was one that emphasised both collaboration and a focus on primary care and which also identified issues with the supply and demand for health care services in Wales. These would continue as themes for NHS Wales underpinning the restructuring of 2001 and into subsequent reviews of health, and then social care in Wales, culminating in the 'Wanless' "Review of Health and Social Care in Wales" of 2003. The policy environment was however not restricted to health but embraced developments in education, most notably the concept of 'lifelong learning' which was of particular pertinence to an organisation which was engaged in developing adults at all stages of their careers.

The business plan therefore emphasises the environment in which the Staff College had to operate. The plan states the need to be aware of the realities of:

- organisational change through trust reconfiguration, White Paper and the proposed National Assembly for Wales;
- pressures in service delivery including developments in health care and force of emergency measures;
- primary health care development including Local Health Groups;
- diverse financial pressure

The plan reiterated the Staff Colleges Principles which had first been articulated in 1995 and related these to the emergent policy context:

1. *"Improving health through personal development of board members, managers, health care professionals and others and the development of their organisations*
2. *Giving the Service what it wants at a competitive price and at the highest quality*
3. *Working in partnership with others inside and outside the service thereby preventing overlap and duplication of resources*
4. *Being a Staff College without walls a 'virtual organisation'*

5. *Open behaviour where we try to live out what we preach*
6. *Evaluating constantly what we do*
7. *Finding out what is best in other organisations and being 'leading edge' ourselves*
8. *Encouraging equality of opportunity so that people are enabled to fulfil their potential"*

This was placed in the context of the three strategic directions of the College:

- Organisational Change – particularly related to Trust reconfiguration
- Primary Care, Health Authority or related developments
- Personal/Career development for clinical staff

The existing range of work was to be open to critique by participants and changed or terminated where it was questioned. Moreover the College sought to apply principles of improvement even where programmes were not challenged. The management group was to set the strategic direction for the college. Each major area of work was to be led by a fellow of the college who was a senior health service executive. Associates from the health service were to deliver many programmes. Each of these stakeholders was seen to make a valuable contribution in ensuring relevance and quality of work and this continued the emphasis in establishing the new College of the importance of involving key stakeholders thereby gaining their commitment to the continued existence of the College. This strategy also included systematic visits and meetings with Chief Executives, Executive Directors, Chairs and others. All of this was designed to ensure that the college was still fully engaged with the service.

The Business Plan of a year later, given perhaps the consolidation of the New Labour agenda and a waiting period for devolution to be enacted, contained more service oriented influences:

- Service priorities for leadership and development as determined by trust and health authority chief executives
- Recommendations of the Programme and Project Funding Review report
- NHS corporate issues including National Assembly for Wales, development of corporate strategic framework and white and green papers
- The Staff College's own mission and main objectives

By 1999 the Annual Report focused on what was considered to be a significant year in the NHS in Wales because of the:

- National Assembly for Wales
- Commitment to partnership across the public sector
- Recognition of need to work collaboratively
- Expectations of the people of Wales of a health service fit for the new millennium
- Creation and development of Local Health Groups
- Reconfiguration of Trusts
- Establishment of National Institute for Clinical Excellence and the Commission for Health Improvement

The elections to the National Assembly for Wales would significantly shape and change the way in which health care services were planned and delivered in Wales. The proximity of the political process to the NHS is particularly noteworthy as were developments in the stakeholder groups comprising the newly emerging health policy community where local government would come to play a new and particular role. However, links to England were by no means broken. The role of the Treasury in determining public spending would continue to impact on health service funding in Wales as would organisation developments across the border. As England moved to emphasising modernisation NHS Wales moved towards partnership working with the emphasis on public health, health inequalities and community engagement.

Both Business Plans and Annual Reports produced by the College identified the main activities to be undertaken by the College in response to the policy and organisational climate of the time. The first Annual Report of 1997 identified programmes and activities. These spanned familiar development programmes, some of which had been inherited by the College, together with programmes which led to educational qualifications and which had been developed in conjunction with academic institutions, most notably UWCM, and more individual and consultancy based activities. These included:

Development Programmes:

- Clinical Directors
- Nurse Development Programme
- Executive Directors
- Chief Executives
- MDS Annual Conference

- SPRs
- Widening Horizons
- Middle Managers Course
- Management Development Scheme
- Financial Management and Accountancy

Educational Programmes
:

- Postgraduate Certificate in Primary Care Management
- Postgraduate Certificate in Health Services Management
- Postgraduate Diploma in Health Services Management
- MSc in Health Services Management
- Education and Development Bursaries

Supporting the "family of health" in Wales:

- Coaching and career guidance
- Consultancy
- Executive Seminars
- Training and Development materials
- Supporting professional groups at national levels
- Organisational development and learning

By 1998 the Annual Report identified activities in seven more general areas, a number of which would be familiar from the creation of the new College onwards:

- To develop leadership capability of managers, clinicians and others
- Promote lifelong learning and development
- Encourage development activities in individual organisations, between professions and across organisational boundaries
- Deliver first rate development activities including programmes, courses, consultancy and individual guidance
- To create time and space for thinking and reflective practice
- Extend the influence of organisation development and learning
- Undertake academic work in leadership, learning development and change management

Primary care activity was particularly championed in this report and was described as "A Mexican Wave of Champions" with active learning and multi sector participation using 'visual facilitation' techniques.

These activities were more specifically elucidated in the Business Plan of that year:

- To support the Welsh Office for its transfer to the National Assembly for Wales; expert advice and consultancy in change management, personal development, career counselling, recruitment and selection, individual consultancy projects, executive coaching, Board Development programme.
- New areas of work: Senior Management Development Programme, Succession Planning, Portfolio Careers, with IHSM course for new and supervisory staff addressing fundamentals of health services management; Continue existing management development programmes, Chief Executive Programme, Executive Director Programme, Leaders from Within, Widening Horizons, general and financial graduate management development programmes, Executive Seminars
- Work with UWCM on Postgraduate Certificate, Diploma and MSc in health services management, franchising and accrediting its educational programmes and build on university partnerships and to publish articles
- Inter-Agency Co-operation: primary care team development; independent facilitators and advisors in development and evaluation of primary care pilots; assist in development of locality commissioning; franchising or accrediting educational programmes; specific events
- Clinician Development: Clinical Director Development Programme; Specialist Registrar Training Programme; Medical Directors Conference; Building Bridges (Nurse Development Programme). Also develop programmes for hospital consultants, Professions Allied to Medicine (PAMs), Ambulance Trust.

The emergence of inter-agency co-operation is to be particularly noted from this and reflected an emerging Welsh emphasis on joint working in particular between health and local government, notably social services. The College saw its activities being potentially expanded from the health arena into making links and working with those within local government and organisations such as SYNIAD which provided training and development opportunities for local authorities. The development of clinical programmes to include PAMs also represented a growth in the College's commitment to engaging a wider range of people in managing and leading the NHS.

The Business Plan of 1999 had 4 Key Themes:

1. Leadership Development: including a series of commitments for Leaders from Within, Management and Finance Graduate Training Schemes, nurses, clinical directors, LHG Chairs, boards and top teams
2. Career Development: Chief Executive development programme, Widening Horizons, new hospital consultant programme, specialist registrars course, Building Bridges for nurses, career counselling, coaching and mentoring, development centres and a range of qualifications
3. Organisation Development: consultancy services, expert advice, commissioned interventions, identification of best practice, personal and practice development planning, inter-sectoral collaboration and promotion of lifelong learning
4. Organisational Learning: executive seminars, creation of centre for organisational learning, learning waves, systems modelling, work associated with corporate strategy, think tanks, increased writing and teaching, further research and evaluation, extension of action learning

The Staff College was developing from an organisation, which for some was associated with the delivery of programmes, into wider organisational interventions and concepts of learning and, as will be seen, into research and evaluation. The place for people to think and develop new ideas and ways of doing things was coming to fruition. However, this was of itself to present challenges to the position of the organisation within the corporate nature of the NHS.

The role of leaders of healthcare drawn from all sectors of NHS staff was now to dominate staff college thinking. Expectations of change and service improvement and greater responsiveness now lay on their shoulders. The concept of service improvement was one which had dominated thinking in the English NHS but was also to find resonance in Wales. The Staff College provided a range of development activities to support this:

- Range of clinical development programmes
- Support for primary care development
- Suite of educational qualifications
- Research activities
- Organisation development support
- Consultancy

Time and effort was also invested to develop the college's capability in:

- Leadership development
- Continuing Professional Development (CPD)
- Intersectoral working
- Encouraging reflective practice and learning in action
- Updating of existing programmes and development of new programmes to support service change

As such the college had been organised into five directorates to reflect core business:

- Programmes
- Research and Development
- Primary Care
- Consultancy
- Qualifications

The Annual Report of 2000 was the last exposition of the philosophy and activities of the Staff College before its transformation into the Centre for Health Leadership Wales. The report states that the only reason for the college to exist was to contribute to the NHS' "bottom line" – better health and health services for people in Wales. As part of this mission the following activities were identified:

- UK and International – conferences, relationships with universities, links with local authorities, 360 degree collaborative advantage indicator
- All Wales Work – PAMs programme; Risk Management; Local Development Scheme (alongside graduate selection for current NHS talent); All Wales Nursing Conference 'Realising the Potential'; Primary care professional development; support for LHGs; Research handbook; CPD; e-learning; conferences; maximising clinical performance (a framework for monitoring and assessing performance in Wales)
- Organisational Level – management and professional development of primary care nurses; practice development planning in primary care; involving patients and carers in the redesign of care pathways; emergency admissions and joined up thinking; steps to successful selection
- Individual – personal development, career development services, psychologists, bursaries

Specialist services being offered included recruitment centres; leadership assessment centres; occupational psychology services; health service policy research; bursaries for continuing education; research into leadership; conference management; team development and facilitation; organisational development; individual mentoring and career guidance; IM&T; consultancy; care pathways and redesign; systems modelling; professional and practice development; GP practice organisational audits; facilitation of action learning; management studies skills training; and CPD.

The issue of academic links was one which had occupied minds since the genesis of the College. It was also an issue which was to prove difficult to resolve. There was a clear view that the Chief Executive of the College should also hold a professorial post in order to demonstrate academic linkage and credibility. This was ultimately achieved by the University of Glamorgan vesting the Staff College Chief Executive with an External Professorship.

A key role was played in the College by both the Management Group and College Fellows. The Management Group oversaw the operational activity and strategy of the College, agreed its business plans, ensured corporate governance and maintained and developed its activities. The group was composed of managers and clinicians drawn from a range of backgrounds and locations who were able to act in a similar way to Non Executive Directors within Trusts working together with the Chief Executive of the Staff College. For a list of initial Management Group members see Appendix 2. The expert chairing of the group allowed for a creative tension and a 'critical friend' approach to develop. Moreover it was intended that members of the group would act as 'goodwill ambassadors' for the College and ensure continued commitment and support from the NHS itself. As has been seen this was critical in establishing the College and would continue to be so in its continued development.

The College Fellows also played an important role in supporting and promoting the College and in helping with the development and promotion of College activities. Fellows supported specific areas of Staff College activities and were very closely and personally linked with the promotion and delivery of their specific area of activity. For a list of Fellows see Appendix 3. Fellows were also provided with a number of opportunities for their own personal and career development. The growth in the role and effectiveness of the Staff College was also aided by the active support of Stephen Redmond, the NHS Director of Human Resources.

The Staff College of 2000 was therefore very different from that of 1995. The number of activities undertaken had grown exponentially spanning a range of activities which reflected both some of the original ideas of the college, as a place for new and cutting edge thinking, through to schemes and programmes quickly and flexibly developed in response to new policy and organisational imperatives.

8

Staff College Programmes

The area of activity which the College was most commonly associated with was its delivery of training and development programmes. The College ran a range of programmes on both a short and longer term basis. Some programmes, such as those for graduates in general management and finance, had existed for many years and had been inherited by the college. Others were innovative for the college ranging from those for clinicians (from specialist registrars through to medical directors together with nurses and professions allied to medicine) through to risk managers. The association of the College with the delivery of programmes had both positive and negative connotations. Development schemes were clearly a key activity for the college and one which other activities, such as research, could support. Moreover, they provided the financial foundations for the College with many people within NHS Wales having an attachment to the College as alumni. This was something which the college sought to formally develop through its alumni links. There were however continuing tensions with local providers of training and development schemes and questioning regarding the legitimacy of other activities.

However, developing new models of learning and of content development was a key concern for those planning, organising and delivering the programmes within the College. Iterative and self directed approaches to learning were complemented in programmes by more structured modular inputs exploring key theories and models of good practice. The College saw a number of different approaches to different client groups including:

Premier Programme:this programme for senior managers adopted a cohort model where 15 people collaborated and worked together to develop their skills and knowledge. The programme was based on three main themes: new directions in health policy, changing face of health care delivery, towards personal mastery.

Primary Care Development:a practice development tool to co-ordinate developments in primary care was pioneered by the College,

This reflected a continued commitment to developing those working within primary care in order to particularly assist with the primary care led notion of health care commissioning. The scheme sought to assist in establishing practice-based clinical governance, maximising contributions to Local Health Groups and providing a framework for managing change and minimising bureaucracy. The development tool worked through five stages from initial briefing to diagnosis and priority setting to problem analysis to implementation and finally to review and evaluation. The tool sought to link the development of the GPs practice with personal and professional development of all team members.

Clinical Director Programme: As part of the commitment to assist clinicians at all stages of their development this programme focused on those heading up the clinical directorate structure. The programme aimed to enhance and develop the role of Clinical Directors and to enable them to become more effective and influential and thus make a substantial contribution to the success of their directorate and ultimately their Trust. The programme had been established in 1997 to encourage a strong medical managerial culture in NHS Wales following several think tanks exploring the issue in 1996. The objectives of the programme centred around providing a contemporary and relevant foundation programme, encouraging development of positive role models for junior staff and helping to prepare the next generation of medical managers. This was a 5 module programme over 4 months addressing the key issues of people and financial management, facilitating an opportunity to practice skills and obtain guidance for self development. Participants were supported by the Staff College through the use of action learning sets and mentors. Each module was accredited by continuing medical education, an important requirement if medical involvement was required, with on average twelve participants on each cohort drawn from a diverse range of professional clinical backgrounds

The Effective Consultant: This programme recognised the importance of all consultants having access to leadership and management development primarily in order to impact positively on patient care. The programme provided participants with a foundation knowledge of management issues and gave them tools with which to be effective clinical managers. The overarching aim of the programme was to encourage clinicians to engage in management and to encourage the development of positive role models for medical staff.

Leaders from Within: This programme was introduced in 1998 as a result of a series of think tanks of senior health services leaders in 1997. The main purpose was to identify and develop current potential within health services in Wales in order to meet the leadership challenges of the next millennium. An 18 month programme was designed to utilise an average 2 days per month of participants' time with development achieved via a range of experiences including challenging assignments, feedback and coaching and a programme of management modules. Use of resources and opportunities within the service were maximised with experience on key strategic development projects providing a foundation to individual learning. Candidates were selected, following rigorous procedures, who were considered to have the potential to become Chief Executives.

Widening Horizons: This programme was well established, since 1992, when it entered the Staff College portfolio. Cohorts of on average 14 participants from a wide range of professional backgrounds undertook a programme that had wide support within the NHS in Wales. The objectives of the programme were to provide exposure to new perspectives, increased self awareness, time to reflect and put ideas 'into practice' and help in taking control of personal development. The programme had an 18 month duration with a mixture of modular learning and on the job application. Learning was shared in the group at open discussion sessions with action learning sets and mentors providing a foundation for further developmental support. Modular content included the main and familiar managerial topics adapted to current policy directives. Participants were very much involved in directing the emphasis of the modules and the programme was designed to provide a safe environment for participants to explore their needs and develop their own PDPs.

Both 'Leaders from Within' and 'Widening Horizons' were located in the mechanisms by which NHS Wales decided to tackle its succession planning needs. The health service had traditionally been very hierarchically organised and succession reflected this. Research demonstrated that changes needed to be made to this traditional model emphasising the need to develop pools of talent from which future appointment could be made. These programmes in particular were an attempt to do that and to respond to the succession planning needs of the health service in Wales.

Graduate training schemes: Training schemes for graduates, and for some in-house candidates, predominantly in general management and financial management had been inherited by the Staff College and had been running in Wales for many years under different guises. They formed an important backbone to the College not merely in the funding provided but as the vehicle by which many senior managers within NHS Wales had entered the service and continued to engage as mentors to trainees. Whilst the schemes had been subjected to criticisms of elitism they continued to have strong support within the NHS despite the changing roles of health services managers.

In addition to the major flagship programmes described above the following offers a selection of other programme activities:

Chief Executive Development: The need to develop all those in the NHS including those who had reached the top of the career ladder was recognised as being important particularly if these individuals were to maintain their enthusiasm and impact on the service. Chief Executive development was therefore personally oriented towards the needs of individuals and the opportunities for sharing learning.

Executive Directors Programme: For those at NHS Trust or Health Authority Board level the College offered some structured interventions and self managed development.

Transformation: Managing Change in the NHS: This was part of the 'Building Bridges' programme which demonstrated an increasing interest in developing nurses in Wales.

Managing Change in Clinical Practice: Aimed at clinicians at all levels, this short programme of one two day block with a follow up day three to four months later focusing on skills in change management.

Primary Care: the development challenges: As part of the commitment to developing primary care commissioning this development programme worked with the principle of 'Waves of Learning' amongst those working in LHGs.

Executive Seminars: As part of its remit to provide a forum for cutting edge thinking these seminars offered senior managers the opportunity to hear speakers of international repute discussing key issues of the time.

The programmes undertaken by the College demonstrated a commitment to long standing and new areas of concern to the NHS spanning clinician through to primary care development. The range of programmes sought to reach participants at all stages of their careers from entering the NHS as trainees through to personally tailored Chief Executive development and offering a range of learning and content to reflect this.

9

An Evidence Base for the Staff College

Training and development interventions must always be questioned in terms of their value to the organisation. The financial costs of engaging in these activities is significant and must be related to the benefits achieved not just by the individual participants but also by their organisations. In the NHS the need to demonstrate an impact on improved patient experience or service improvement is the key measure by which any intervention may be judged. It is however, very difficult to make the link between training and development and improvements in service and patient outcome. The Programme and Projects review of 1998 had required the college to engage in evaluation which would determine the value of the college's interventions to the individual when they returned to the workplace. This was to be underpinned by evaluation and the establishment of a research and evidence base for management, leadership and organisation development and this came to form an important part of the college's modus operandi.

The difficulties of evaluating interventions particularly when looking at attitudinal and cultural changes, as opposed to acquisition of skills and knowledge, were acknowledged by the College in drafting its evaluation methodology. The college proposed a 3 pronged approach to the evaluation of programmes:

- Preparation of a service led specification
- Module evaluation
- Behavioural outcomes

Behavioural outcomes were seen to be the most complex with the college moving towards using these by recognising several key issues:

-need for evaluation to have more immediate and practical use
-use of fewer resources and short timescale for results

-more flexible approach to collecting information
-more attention to subjective experiences of participants and
sponsors

Evaluation design was seen not to have a dichotomous outcome
(either valued or not) but needing multiple criteria to assess outcomes. Context, Administration, Inputs, Processes, and Outcomes
(CAIPO) was proposed as the framework for all evaluation. Programme outcomes and participant and service gain were all seen to
be critical and would remain the primary focus. It was felt that there
was a need to be flexible and take account of evolving culture and
service developments. Closed loop feedback would be provided as
would a form of 'developmental evaluation' which was both iterative
and action oriented. Evaluation was not to be governed by rigid ex-
perimental principles but observing best practice advice. The evaluation was intended to contribute whilst the training or developmental
intervention were being carried out thereby providing immediate
feedback. Evaluation was to be locally based, collaborative, action
based, qualitative and inductive.

Evaluation was to be undertaken on three levels and the focus of
this was to be:

-What positive changes occurred?
-Is the change due to the development programme?
-What is required to ensure such positive change will occur
with future participants in the same programme?

From these principles and methodological perspective the College
established a rolling programme of evaluation. Three programmes
were subjected to this in-depth evaluation:

Leaders from Within: A case study approach was used allowing in-depth discussions regarding individual needs, programme
structure and development outcomes with each participant. Each
participant was interviewed at length regarding their experience on
the programme, its content, administration and structure as well as
discussion about benefits gained by each participant. Quantitative
information using bespoke questionnaires – leadership skills inven-
tory review and emotional intelligence review – was also obtained.

The evaluation revealed strong developmental inputs emerging
from the programme including:

- Leadership courses
- Individual feedback for participants on leadership style
- Arena for discussion and debate on major influences upon the leadership of the Welsh NHS

Overall the programme's strength was in supporting leadership development whilst providing a Welsh backdrop for the consideration of leadership. Breadth of benefit across the 3 participants was revealed illustrating the comprehensiveness of the programme. A strong development trend was demonstrated in:

- Self confidence
- Understanding leaders personal dilemmas and challenges
- Effective leadership styles
- Self awareness

The programme was seen as a powerful model of reflective learning facilitating a greater understanding of how leaders do and the characteristics of leaders as compared to what leaders do. Participant career progression and direct service benefit as a result of the programme were considerable as were the effects on participant awareness and practical leadership skills both during and following the completion of the programme.

UWCM Postgraduate Diploma/MSc Health Services Evaluation 2000: The consultancy module of this joint Staff College/UWCM course was evaluated. A focus group approach was used for 2 student intakes (1998 and 1999) with a structured approach using individual reflection, small group discussion and whole group feedback. Content analysis was conducted on the findings. The CAIPO evaluation framework was used. Major benefits identified were teamworking, team management and understanding team dynamics. Key learning was also achieved in understanding of the health service and problem solving.

Widening Horizons Development Programme Evaluation 2000: This was a well established programme with a long history. A bespoke questionnaire designed to measure actual change in participant managerial behaviours was used. Improvement in the managerial behaviours in the workplace was examined at the first level of analysis. 50 items, 10 for each of the 5 modules of the programme, were graded to allow a second level of analysis – improved knowledge, understanding and use of positive behaviours. Where actual change occurred, whether at basic knowledge level or at a higher strategic and application level, this was identified. The development questionnaire had a hierarchical formulation of questions, as recommended by psychological literature, on behaviourally anchored rating scales (BARS) was used throughout questions to test applications of required skills and behaviours. As the evaluation sought to measure actual behavioural change, as compared to knowledge, questions were framed as behavioural statements and participants were required to comment on the frequency with which they practised the particular behaviour. The following scale was used:

6   -always behaves as described
5-   mostly behaves as described
4-   sometimes behaves as described
3-   rarely behaves as described
2-   never behaves as described
1 – not appropriate or insufficient knowledge/opportunity

Participants were also canvassed regarding the support they had received and required whilst undertaking the programme. Benefits to the service were also captured and examples provided. A final questionnaire was also sent out. The evaluation focused on quantifiable managerial improvement and service benefits and examined relative value of programme support elements. Initial evaluation demonstrated the widespread success of the programme in identifying and meeting developmental needs and participants. Participants reported a comprehensive improvement in their consistency in applying and understanding positive managerial practices. Particular benefit was derived from the Finance and Information and Strategy modules. The second level of evaluation revealed in every module the development of higher functions of managerial activities – this suggests not only the acquisition of knowledge and understanding but actual behavioural changes and direct service benefit.

A number of other areas benefited from an evidence based approach including:

"Graduate Management and Leadership Development in NHS Staff College Wales" this report by Cranfield University School of Management used a literature review, focus group interviews, questionnaires and telephone interviews. It concluded that recruiting and retaining graduates had become increasingly difficult and that the nature of the employment relationship had shifted visibly. Graduates had become increasingly powerful and demanding. This, it was suggested, needed a stronger and more coherent strategic vision and

mission for fast track recruitment and development. Wide variation in training experiences were ascribed to a lack of 'corporate' vision. Marketing could convey a stronger message about the uniqueness of the programmes and the size and profile of NHS Wales. Most organisations did not employ tracking procedures or measures which would enable them objectively to evaluate the effectiveness of their recruitment or training. The report recommended re-examining what the scheme was meant to achieve; how it would benefit NHS Wales; where it would fit into overall human resources plans; and standards by which experiences and placements would be evaluated. The report also discussed the scope and remit of the College and the need to put in place some processes to track the quality of recruitment, selection and trainee experience. This was reiterated in the Leadership Development Programme Review which gave recommendations that any programme should clarify: aims; customers; context; overall processes; detailed approach and outcomes.

In addition to formal evaluations of programmes and activities the College spread its net wider in developing a range of 'think pieces' and evidence based resources. 'Think Tanks' with prepared papers and drawing on the experiences of key stakeholders were held on areas such as Locality Commissioning and Succession Planning and the findings written up. The College also developed its own research and evidence based briefing papers the first of which was "Effective Models of Commissioning: The Evidence". This was designed to fit with a mission to disseminate ideas and good practice throughout the NHS and beyond and also to potentially give the College a place on a wider academic and practitioner stage.

The College also sought to develop its role in relation to research. This reflected a view that there was a place for the organisation to undertake research in policy, organisational and management areas which dated back to the first genesis of the idea for the college. By 1999 the strategy for research within the college had two main strands:

- Developing managers' awareness and use of research.
  This recognised that clinical colleagues were expected to incorporate research and evidence based findings into their practice but that this had been a poorly developed field in management. A key role the College took was to develop understandings of the philosophies of research and of research tools. This also included developing the ability to access evidence and understand what constituted evidence

and to critically appraise and ultimately apply evidence based practice.

- Developing the research base in policy, organisation development, leadership and management. Part of the difficulty in getting managers to use evidence lay in the limited amount of research, as opposed to theoretically based work, that had emerged in these fields. The College took a role in undertaking and to a limited extent commissioning and disseminating research to add to this body of knowledge.

The College undertook a number of activities in relation to this including research into primary care developments, continuing professional development, commissioning and leadership. This resulted both in papers published and conference presentations and in wider dissemination to the NHS and broader community. At the same time a series of evidence based management workshops ran for health services managers which provided an introduction to evidence and gave hands on experience in accessing, interpreting and critiquing evidence for managers. This was accompanied by the development, in conjunction with the Wales Office for Research and Development and the Institute of Healthcare Management, of a research handbook for managers which included an introduction to research tools, details of ongoing research training and projects and the development of a network of active researchers within the healthcare management community. The College also noted the place of research in underpinning the development of its programmes and for example undertook specific work in researching Top Team and Non Executive Board Member development. This diverse range of evidence based resources demonstrated the commitment of the college to developing an evidence base not just in terms of evaluating its own programmes but in providing a deeper level of understanding in leadership, management, organisation development and policy.

10

Reviewing the College

Reflecting perhaps some of the difficulties experienced in actually establishing the college, the Staff College was itself a recipient of a number of reviews as to its purpose, funding and activities. 1998 saw the college undergo a review of its programmes and projects (reporting in 1999) which drew on a series of key influences:

* Service priorities: in particular the change management agenda arising out of trust mergers
* Primary care development particularly LHGs
* Leadership Development
* Organisational Development
* Personal Development
* Clinical Governance

The review found that:

* There should be a formal business plan, although business plans had been produced since the College's inception in 1995
* Throughput and volume associated with the college's range of programmes should be balanced against other objectives particularly organisation development
* Greater emphasis on organisation development associated with policy development and promulgation.
* Extend the practice of evaluation: present two levels of evaluation to include the ultimate outcome so wherever possible the impact of the development intervention on the individual when returning to the workplace
* Total funding agreed for 1999/2002 in terms of All Wales Schemes, development costs of new initiatives and core staff costs. All other programme activity to be treated on a commercial basis and charging regime introduced, accepting risks were inherent for some staff in this

Service leaders identified the important place of research and development and the developmental need for more reflective thinking. The college was seen to be ideally placed to respond to this. NHS Wales was experiencing major structural re-organisation at both secondary and primary care levels. This rapidly evolving working environment produced uncertainties amongst many engaged in planning and providing services and therefore a focus on short term objectives. But there was a recognised need for longer term reflection to help ensure new structures and policies both appropriate to new situations and based on evidence. Creating opportunities to encourage reflective thinking was seen to be vital in order to make decisions based on evidence of effectiveness and relevance. The need for health services managers to examine the following was identified:

- Extent to which new policies and plans are delivering their objectives
- Extent to which current activities are in line with changing needs
- Extent to which new plans are in line with emerging policy directives

This was to be achieved by a three-pronged approach:

1. Commitment: engaging with the service to engender ownership of and a commitment to developing a strategy to meeting the need for more reflective thinking
2. Skills/capacity: working with the service to develop skills and capacity to think reflectively within busy operational environment
3. Forums/channels: to disseminate learning: hosting think tanks on issues of organisational effectiveness within the Welsh context

There was also some discussion of the academic linkages of the staff college. The college was seen not to be duplicating or competing with academia but developing partnership linkages with it. Various universities inside and outside Wales were included in this partnership as were research, policy and teaching organisations such as the Kings Fund and Ashridge Management College. The benefits to the NHS of the partnership with academia were seen as: access to academics and university libraries, resources and networks; opportunities to develop programmes; opportunities for clinicians and managers to hold honorary or part time appointments; and collaboration. The benefits to academia were: access to organisations for research; real education programmes; placements; steady stream of students; extension of faculty; collaboration; and credibility. A variety of possible linkages were suggested from simple ad hoc through to negotiating 'spheres of influence' with the college having a natural role as broker for NHS Wales to benefit the NHS and its employees.

In 1999/2000 the Staff College was reviewed by the management consultancy firm Deardens who had the brief to look at the college's position, funding and governance in the new NHS Wales. This was a positive review recommending that the college be brought closer to the National Assembly's strategic direction while still remaining an integral part of the NHS Wales *"its funding will be settled and the long term future will be secure"*. This move towards locating the College more clearly with the central government agenda was one which was to cause some tensions. This raises interesting questions regarding the convergence of government and health service agendas and the role and place of public servants. It can also be linked to the emergence of devolution and the desire to create a distinctive Welsh policy and service direction. It is also interesting to speculate why despite the positive outcomes of the reviews the college continued to be reviewed on a regular basis. This, however, reflects a dynamic of organisational change which dominates the NHS, although few organisations were reviewed in the way and as frequently as the Staff College.

In part this may be attributed to the entrepreneurial and flexible way in which the college was established. Growing quickly, yet without much of the infrastructure available to other organisations, the College was vulnerable to continued question asking both over its function and funding. Much of this also related to many of the difficulties faced in trying the establish the College in the first place including issues of central control, 'ownership' of the College, North/ South Wales divide and range of activities. It could also be speculated that the College occupied a very unusual place in what was a large and predominantly bureaucratic organisation – the NHS. The College was increasingly attempting to position itself at the cutting edge of thinking and activities and it is debatable how far such an organisation can ultimately survive within a bigger organisation which, charged with the distribution of public funds, has to impose high levels of controls, systems, processes and accountabilities.

Running alongside the reviews, business plans and annual reports were a series of internal debates on the purpose and role of the Staff College. In 1998 "NHS Staff College Wales – Its purpose and role" identified the context of the college which was seen as organisational, governmental and academic with the college occupying the middle (learning and development) ground between the service, government initiatives and academic knowledge. To support this the college was stated not to have a traditional structure but rather to be flexible, team based and related to activities with project working, matrix relationships, flexibility and personal accountability to the fore. It is interesting to contrast the internal view of the college and the external view which resulted in so many reviews within the history of the College. Ultimately the principles which underpinned the running of the College might have been at odds with an emergent culture in which performance management and more formal lines of business planning and accountabilities were becoming dominant.

Perhaps the most comprehensive internal review of the college is contained in "NHS Staff College Wales: 1999 and Beyond" and "The NHS Staff College Wales: The Potential for the Future" discussion papers. These stated that the new position of the college was more appropriate to the ongoing and emerging development agenda of health services in Wales. The documents sought to take into account changes in structure and running of the NHS; the government's approach to learning and education; and the experience of the Staff College over three and a half years. The purpose of these papers was to promote discussion about how the college could facilitate the modernisation of the NHS and increase its potential impact on the service in the future. The documents demonstrate the College's continuing quest to locate itself within the current policy context:

"When it was established the college was set up within a context of a strong emphasis on the elimination of any unnecessary overhead costs, as part of the 'Redwood' era. The college had a difficult path to tread between establishing the need for development and learning and not being seen to be expansionist and all knowing".

It was recognised that the college had grown and the political climate had changed. It was this growth, both in terms of staff numbers and activities undertaken, that motivated this discussion. To some extent the college ran the risk of becoming the victim of its own success as it grew quickly within the context of what had been a virtual organisation. The following positive attributes of the college were identified:

- A concept which is well established and owned by the Service
- Being faced with a growing demand for products and services
- Offering essential personal development support in a safe and confidential environment

- Providing professional service
- Enjoying credible reputation with NHS stakeholders

The current policy drivers for change were identified:

- Cultural shift towards collaborative working
- Establishment of the National Assembly for Wales
- Introduction of clinical governance
- Recognition of key stakeholders and their sponsorship
- Commitment towards lifelong learning
- All Wales Strategies for example Human Resources and ICT
- Increasing demand for staff college products
- Introduction of National Service Frameworks

It was suggested that the college was in a new phase and should move forward by:

- Playing a strategic role in the development arena across Wales operating in a legitimate/overt way
- Maximising influence to increase return on investment
- Utilising current drivers associated with clinical governance and national service frameworks as a route to improve clinical services and to support organisation development and lifelong learning
- Re-evaluating core values, mission and objectives
- Reviewing existing products and service portfolio
- Organising itself appropriately internally to meet the opportunities presented

The College was correct in identifying that it was entering a very different phase of its existence and this was one which would see the NHS Staff College Wales becoming the Centre for Health Leadership Wales.

11

Conclusions – what can we learn from the Staff College Story?

In the spirit of organisational and personal learning and reflection that was so central to the College in many stages of its development there are many lessons that can be drawn from the genesis, creation, development and ultimately end of the NHS Staff College Wales. This book has sought to trace the history of the college and by doing so to explore some important and more wide reaching issues. It is particularly important that organisational memory is exploited in order to learn lessons for the future. Too often this is lost in organisational change and this book demonstrates the value of telling the story of an organisation. If an evidence base for organisation development and change is to be further developed the stories of developing other organisations will become increasingly important.

The Staff College Wales itself sought to explore these lessons through its discussion papers exploring which as well as exploring its future looked back over the history of the college. The following lessons to be learned were drawn from the development of the college:

- Need to determine 'core' business
- Need to prioritise competing demands
- Need to clarify primary and secondary customers
- Need to improve customers understanding of staff college player roles
- Need to improve internal systems management and operational efficiency
- Need for human resources framework to facilitate staff performance improvement
- Need for clarity about internal structures, roles and lines of accountability
- Need for evidence based and added value focus through robust evaluation frameworks
- Need to manage stakeholder expectations

75

- Need for cultural change allowing for synergised creativity; shared understanding of core values; improved effectiveness and value for money; reduction in negative behaviours associated with lack of role clarity and transparency in decision making; allow talented individuals to maximise their impact

The lessons to be learned can, however, be cast in a wider frame of reference which may be of value to those seeking to set up and establish a similar type of organisation now or in the future:

1.   Creating An Organisation

The Staff College provides a case study on how a new organisation can be created which may be of value to those seeking to establish similar types of organisations in the future. The college emerged as a small and flexible organisation within a much larger and somewhat bureaucratic organisation – the National Health Service. It was however this form which may ultimately have led to its eventual 'de facto' incorporation into the Welsh Assembly Government of the National Assembly for Wales. Throughout its existence the college always had to hold a place at the nexus of government, academia and of course the National Health Service in Wales. Meeting the needs and demands of these different stakeholders was always challenging.

The actual creation of the College demonstrates the importance of seizing opportunities and working innovatively and flexibly to get a development off the ground. The initial history of the College was frustrated by being locked into a series of meetings, business plans and documentation. The establishment of the College occurred by exploiting organisational changes within the NHS and by establishing a small and responsive organisation.

The early Staff College was non hierarchical and developed a range and diversity of activities that were strongly located within the needs of NHS Wales. The College grew rapidly, both in terms of budgets and staff. However, this created tensions with the requirements for infrastructure, mechanisms and accountabilities within the NHS. There must also be some debate regarding whether an organisation like the Staff College can ultimately survive within the constraints of the much larger NHS. This raises a much wider debate about the most effective ways to design organisations, particularly those which sit within much larger organisational systems, to facilitate flexibility and creativity but which are clearly accountable. This may be difficult to achieve as organisations like this are more familiarly found in the private sector, for example in advertising agencies or software companies. However, the links between organisational form and improved user experience and service improvement is a critical one both for the NHS and other public sector organisations.

The physical location of the college was also an issue which was much debated both in its inception and development. Original notions of providing a physical place where the activities of the college could be located gave way to the idea of the virtual college, the "college without walls". It was this model which would allow for the quick establishment of the college and which chimed with the organisational and policy climate of its time. Whilst the college was able to operate relatively successfully within the boundaries of its virtual walls it may have been more advantageous for the college to ultimately have had a physical location. This would have provided a visible location where programme participants, staff and all those engaged in college activities could have met. Moreover it would have allowed for a concentration of resources and a greater synergy in terms of learning. Moreover a physical college would also have provided for a very tangible representation of the credibility and positioning of the organisation which may ultimately have impacted on its development.

2. Corporate Values

The Staff College had a particular role, from its inception onwards, in promoting the corporate values of the NHS. This is however by no means an easy issue. The culture of the NHS is marked by professional tribalism and organisational boundaries and establishing commonalities across these has been challenging. This is reflected in ongoing tensions between centralised directives and decentralised roles, in particular of NHS Trusts. Whilst NHS Wales has existed as a entity for a considerable period of time the introduction of the internal market created different cultural and organisational realities which were to be changed again in the wake of devolution and the establishment of the National Assembly for Wales.

The programmes and services of the College sought to promote a shared value base for NHS Wales. This included the provision of a wide range of programmes for clinicians, in particular medical staff, which sought to break down professional boundaries. There are clearly still questions to be posed regarding methods by which new and existing staff can develop to share a common value base for the NHS. In Wales, this needs to be complemented with discussion regarding partnership values across public and voluntary sector organisations and with the Welsh Assembly Government and National Assembly for Wales. This also needs to be placed within the context of the debate regarding the development of a distinctive Welsh public service.

3.   The role of stakeholders

The story of the Staff College demonstrates the importance of gaining the commitment and ownership of key stakeholders in the health policy community both to create and sustain an organisation like the College which does not have a traditional and long established role within the healthcare sector. The early history of the college was dogged by the limited number of influential champions both within the NHS and the Welsh Office. The creation of the College in 1995 was achieved following an extensive consultation exercise across Wales and by ensuring that key individual stakeholders had a place in the running of the college through the creation of the Management Group and the College Fellows. The recognition of involving stakeholders beyond those of general managers, in particular to clinicians both medics and nurses, was also particularly noteworthy in establishing and developing the College.

4.   Policy Climate

Understanding the history of the Staff College also requires an understanding of the policy climate within which public sector organisations, in particular, have to operate. Failure to analyse and understand the policy environment can pose major problems as demonstrated by the early history of the College. The more centralised approach of this period was increasingly at odds with the decentralised notions of the introduction of the internal market which sought in particular, at least in the early stages, to devolve power to NHS Trusts. The election of New Labour and the emergent political and policy context which underpinned devolution in Wales was to create a new policy paradigm. This was one in which corporate Welsh government values and an emphasis on collaboration and partnership were to become dominant. The development of strong emphases on governance and performance management were also to impact on the flexible market oriented Staff College and to contribute in its reinvention as the Centre for Health Leadership. The history of the

Staff College demonstrates the importance of understanding both political and policy processes for those working, in particular in public sector organisations, and combining these with understandings of organisation, management and leadership theories and practice.

5.   Research and Evidence Base

The Staff College sought to emphasise the need for an evidence base for management, leadership and organisation development. These are fields which are notably under researched and the College's work both in raising awareness amongst managers of the role of research in underpinning their practice and in developing a research base to assist with this were important activities. Demonstrating the impact of training and development interventions themselves were important activities within an organisation such as the NHS, where every penny diverted from direct patient care is questioned. The College made initial progress in developing evaluations of their programmes although it was recognised ultimately some demonstration of the impact of these interventions on service delivery would need to be established. There is still a considerable need to develop the evidence base for management, leadership and organisation development, although understanding the ways in which evidence can be constructed and ensuring that innovation is not stifled are also important messages. Investing in robust research in these areas is likely to bear significant dividends as will ensuring that major service changes are subjected to robust evaluation mechanisms.

6.   Training and Development Interventions

The Staff College sought to move away from the model of a training centre to a much wider understanding of learning and development. The College should be particularly noted for its role in developing programmes for clinicians. This resulted for example in many medical staff being touched by the College's programmes from Registrars through to Medical Directors. This was coupled with the provision of a range of programmes both for nurses and professions allied to medicine. In a small country like Wales this allows for a sharing of corporate values and understandings across a range of professional groups who may not always have been comfortable with ideas around management and leadership. Challenges continue to be posed for those who seek to offer training and development interventions to ensure that new methods for delivering these, for example in e-learning, are maximised and that benefits for the individual, organisation, patient and public are articulated.

7. Developing Human Capital

Recognising the importance of human and intellectual capital is an important challenge for contemporary organisations and one which the College sought to embrace. Intellectual capital is often considered to include knowledge management and to refer basically to the human beings working within the organisation, the intelligence and data held within the organisation and the various networks the organisation can utilise. The NHS remains a labour intensive organisation in which the knowledge, skills and experiences of its staff have a major contribution to make to service improvement. Developing staff in a way that maximises their intellectual capital particularly in times of rapid organisational change and loss of organisational memory is critical and perhaps one of the most important challenges and legacies of the Staff College.

Postscript

As has been seen, the advent of devolution in Wales in 1999 was to make for a different approach to health and health services. However, this took some time to emerge. The early years of the Assembly saw a minority Labour government which made policy making and implementation difficult. Moreover the Assembly was on a steep learning curve exploring the limits of its powers. The coalition between Labour and the Liberal Democrats led to a government which could more easily enact policies and in a familiar pattern to many other governments this saw a reorganisational change for the NHS in Wales.

2001 saw the publication of a national plan for the NHS in Wales – "Improving Health in Wales: A Plan for the NHS and its Partners". The plan highlighted the importance of a primary care led NHS with joint working particularly between the NHS and local government as a key lever for change. The Plan made partnership working between the NHS, through newly established Local Health Boards and Local Authorities, a statutory responsibility demonstrated in the construction of a Health, Social and Well Being Plan. Organisationally, this resulted in the abolition of the Welsh Health Authorities replaced with 22 Local Health Boards coterminous with their Local Authority counterparts. 'Improving Health in Wales' also emphasised the role leaders across all health and social care professions would have to play in the new organisation.

In recognition of its role, and unanticipated by its staff, the NHS Staff College Wales became the Centre for Health Leadership Wales.

Appendix 1

Heronston Meeting Invitees

Mr J Wyn Owen   Director of the NHS in Wales

Miss M P Bull   Chief Nursing Officer, Welsh Office

Mr G Davies   HMSP 1 Division, Welsh Office

Mr J Button   District General Manager, West Glamorgan Health Authority

Dr A Jones   Industrial Training Service

Professor W Williams   Chairman, West Glamorgan Health Authority

Dr M Warner   Executive Director, Welsh Health Planning Forum

Dr C Potter   Director, Manpower Consultancy Service

Mr D Mowbray   Director, Management Advisory Service

Dr G Jones   Gareth Jones and Associates

Mr S Prosser   Director, Organisation Development, East Dyfed Health Authority

Appendix 2
Management Group

Chairman:	Paul Williams, Chief Executive, Bridgend and DistrictNHS Trust
Ms Sue Gregory	Executive Director of Nursing, Gwent Community Health NHS Trust
Dr John Wyn Jones	GP, Montgomery Medical Practice
Mr Mike Ponton	Managing Director, Dyfed Health Authority
Mr Stephen Prosser	Chief Executive, NHS Staff College Wales
Mr Bill Ravenscroft	Chief Executive, North Wales Ambulance NHS Trust
Mr Clive Sparkes	Consultant Audiological Scientist, Glan Clwyd District General Hospital NHS Trust
Ms Jan Williams	Chief Executive, Llanelli/Dinefwr NHS Trust
Ms Shona Sullivan	Clinical Director, East Glamorgan Hospital NHS Trust
Ex officio	Director of Finance, Morriston Hospital NHS Trust
Ex officio	Chief Executive, Morriston Hospital NHS Trust

Appendix 3
NHS Staff College Fellows

Glyn Griffiths	Lead on issues concerning Staff College training schemes
Bob Hudson	Worked with College in setting up new programmes for Middle Managers
Julie Gregory	Lead on issues in primary care
Martin Turner	Lead on Executive Directors Programme and on Doctors in Management
Jeremy Hallett	Worked on new programme for High Fliers
Gail Williams	Worked on areas of mentoring and self development and on Doctors in Management
Mike Ponton	Fellow 'without portfolio' to utilise OD expertise
Jonathan Davies	Lead in identifying best practice in personal and organisational Development in other sectors and new ways of delivering Development
Peter Higson	Interest in people, careers and organisations in transition and Learning from success and failure
Stephanie Matthews	Lead in learning from re-configurations particularly for clinicians
Georgina Gordon	Worked on nurse leadership issues

ISBN 141202925-2